MW00651215

CREATING HEALTHY HABITS FOR LIFE

Part 2

C·R·E·A·T·I·O·N Health

LIFE GUIDE #7

For Individual Study and Small Group Use

creation®
HEALTH

CREATION Health Life Guide #7
Copyright © MMXII by Florida Hospital
Published by Florida Hospital Publishing
900 Winderley Place, Suite 1600
Maitland, Florida 32751

To Extend *the* Health *and* Healing Ministry *of* Christ

Publisher and Editor-in-Chief:	Todd Chobotar
Managing Editor:	David Biebel, DMin
Production:	Lillian Boyd
Promotion:	Laurel Dominesey
Copy Editor:	Mollie Braga
Photographer:	Timothy Brown
Design:	Carter Design, Inc.
Peer Reviewers:	Bradford Eakins, MDiv; Robert Hayes
	Gerald Wasmer, MDiv; Greg Ellis, MDiv
	Mary Lou Caskey; Sabine Vatel, DMin
	Andy McDonald, DMin; Tim Goff, MDiv
	Rick Szilagyi, DMin; James Dill, MD
	Andre VanHeerden; Paul Campoli, MDiv
	Jeff Cinquemani, MA; Eric Doran, DMin

PUBLISHER'S NOTE: This book is not intended to replace a one-on-one relationship with a qualified healthcare professional, but as a sharing of knowledge and information from the research and experience of the author. You are advised and encouraged to consult with your healthcare professional in all matters relating to your health and the health of your family. The publisher and author disclaim any liability arising directly or indirectly from the use of this monograph.

The author assumes full responsibility for the accuracy of all facts and quotations as cited in this book. CREATION Health is a registered trademark of Florida Hospital. All rights reserved.

NOT TO BE REPRODUCED
No portion of this book may be reproduced, stored in a retrieval system, or transmitted in any form or by any means – electronic, mechanical, photocopy, recording, or any other – except for brief quotations in printed reviews, without the prior written permission of the publisher. All rights reserved.

Unless otherwise indicated, all Scripture quotations are taken from the Holy Bible, New Living Translation, copyright © 1996, 2004 by Tyndale House Publishers, Inc., Wheaton, Illinois 60189. All other Scripture references are from the following sources: The Holy Bible, New International Version (NIV), copyright © 1973, 1978, 1984 by Biblica, Inc. Used by permission of Zondervan. The Holy Bible, Revised Standard Version (RSV), copyright © 1946, 1952, 1971 by the National Council of the Churches of Christ. The Holy Bible, King James Version (KJV). The Holy Bible, New King James Version (NKJV), copyright © 1982 by Thomas Nelson, Inc. The Message (MSG), copyright© by Eugene H. Peterson 1993, 1994, 1995, 1996, 2000, 2001, 2002. Used by permission of NAVPress Publishing Group. All Scriptures used by permission. All rights reserved.

For volume discounts please contact special sales at:
HealthProducts@FLHosp.org | 407-303-1929

Cataloging-in-Publication Data for this book
is available from the Library of Congress.
Printed in the United States of America.
PR 14 13 12 11 10 9 8 7 6 5 4 3 2 1
ISBN: 978-0-9839881-3-7

For more life-changing resources visit:
FloridaHospitalPublishing.com
Healthy100Churches.org
CREATIONHealth.com
Healthy100.org

CONTENTS

Introduction – Welcome to *CREATION* Health   4

1. Amazing Resources   6

2. Failing Successfully   16

3. Inside Your Brain   28

4. Belief Busters   40

5. Handling the Heckler   52

6. Learning to Say "No"   64

7. Harness Your Full Mind   74

8. Staying Power   86

About the Author   101

Notes   102

Resources   105

Note to Reader: *This second set of eight lessons is Part 2 of the habit formation series. These lessons are intended to follow the eight lessons in Part 1. All of the lessons are built on the letters "C" (Choice) and "O" (Outlook) from the acronym "CREATION."*

DOWNLOAD YOUR FREE LEADER RESOURCE

Are you a small group leader? We've created a special resource to help you lead an effective CREATION Health discussion group. Download at: **CREATIONHealth.com/LeaderResources**

WELCOME TO CREATION HEALTH

Congratulations on your choice to use this resource to improve your life! Whether you are new to the concept of CREATION Health or are a seasoned expert, this book was created for you. CREATION Health is a faith-based health and wellness program based on the Bible's Creation story. This book is part of a Life Guide series seeking to help you apply eight elegantly simple principles for living life to the full.

The letters of the CREATION acronym stand for:

C CHOICE

R REST

E ENVIRONMENT

A ACTIVITY

T TRUST

I INTERPERSONAL

O OUTLOOK

N NUTRITION

In John 10:10 Jesus said, "I have come that they may have life, and have it to the full" (NIV). The Greek word used for life is "zoe," which means the absolute fullness of life…genuine life…a life that is active, satisfying, and filled with joy.

That is why CREATION Health takes a life-transforming approach to total person wellness – mentally, physically, spiritually and socially – with the eight universal principles of health. Where did these principles come from?

The book of Genesis describes how God created the earth and made a special garden called Eden as a home for his first two children, Adam and Eve. One of the first and finest gifts given to them was abundant health. By examining the Creation story we can learn much about feeling fit and living long, fulfilling lives today.

As you begin this journey toward an improved lifestyle, remember that full health is more than the absence of disease and its symptoms. It's a realization that God desires each of his children – people like you and me whom he loves and cares about – to have the best that this life can offer. It is trusting that your Creator has a plan for your life.

Is there any good parent who doesn't want the best for their child? No. So it makes sense that God would want his best for us. Naturally, human freedom of choice sometimes makes life messy, so not everything can or will be perfect as it once was. But that doesn't mean we shouldn't take a good look at the earliest records of humans found in the Bible to see if there is something special that can be gleaned.

This book – and the other seven in the Life Guide series – takes a deep dive into CREATION Health and translates the fundamental concepts into easy-to-follow steps. These guides include many questions designed to help you or your small group plumb the depths of every principle and learn strategies for integrating the things you learn into everyday life. As a result, you will discover that embracing the CREATION Health prescription can help restore health, happiness, balance, and joy to life.

The CREATION Health Lifestyle has a long, proven history of wellness and longevity – worldwide! People just like you are making a few simple changes in their lives and living longer, fuller lives. They are getting healthy, staying healthy, and are able to do the things they love, well into their later years. Now is the time to join them by transforming your habits into a healthy lifestyle.

If you would like to learn more about the many resources available, visit **CREATIONHealth.com**. If you would like to learn more about how to live to a Healthy 100, visit **Healthy100.org** or visit **Healthy100Churches.org**.

Welcome to CREATION Health,

Todd Chobotar
Publisher and Editor-in-Chief

AMAZING RESOURCES

LESSON ONE

WARM UP

Choose one or both questions to discuss (if in group setting)
or write out your answers on a separate sheet (for individual use):

1. **Tell about a time when you got locked out of your home or car.**[1]

    ....
    ....
    ....
    ....
    ....
    ....

2. **Give your description of the perfect day.**[2]

    ....
    ....
    ....
    ....
    ....
    ....

"Never lose an opportunity
of seeing anything beautiful,
for beauty is
God's handwriting."

RALPH WALDO EMERSON

DISCOVERY

This lesson opens our understanding to the amazing spiritual resources that can be ours simply for the asking. These resources were designed by God to help get you to your abundant living destination. Too many people attempt habit change without them and as a result get mired down in unnecessary struggles. We are delving more fully into the spiritual dimension here because we want you to have access to every available means of support.

Back in the mid-1980s, I nearly died twice in one week. Without any experience whatsoever, I had decided to take down some of the 100-foot-tall pine trees around our home in rural Maine.

The first tree stood on the side of a ravine at the edge of our property. It towered over me. Bracing myself in an uneven stance, I held the small, electric, toy-like chainsaw my parents had given me against the thick tree bark and pulled the trigger. It whirred away for minutes, but was about as effective as a toothless person gumming an uncooked ear of corn.

My life took a precarious turn when I eventually purchased a real gas powered chainsaw and tackled the same tree again. *Piece of cake*, I thought, since it was already leaning downhill. About half way through, I heard a loud "CRRAAACK" and it started to go. I glanced upward and noticed to my horror that the top fifteen feet was not following the rest of the tree. Rotten, it broke off and fell straight down toward my tender little body. Panicked, I scrambled up the severely sloping ground. The wayward segment landed close enough to scrape along my back and then tumbled away.

I can usually take a hint. But not this time. On another day, I decided to attempt another tree without such a formidable girth. This one had fallen in a storm and wedged itself between two other trees ending up about five feet above the ground. *Piece of cake*, I thought. I cut into it not realizing that it had become twisted creating enormous tension like a dangerous, heavy-duty, coiled-up spring. As my saw sliced through, the tree sprang back in my direction, missing my face by no more than a couple of life-saving inches.

I *can* take two, really big hints. So I contacted a genuine tree man. He arrived the next day with lots of equipment – bigger chain saws, helmet with ear protectors and face protector, axes, ropes, chains, pullies, a "Come Along," climbing boots, elbow and shin protectors, etc. Wow. He really knew his stuff. Efficient and effective. We partnered together. How foolish I felt to have attempted such a daunting task on my own.

My ill-advised gambit with the trees has served as a stark reminder that we were never intended to go it alone when tackling significant challenges in life, especially such personal challenges as creating new habits. Thankfully, we are given ready access to wonderful divine assistance. God takes a personal interest in our abundant living journey and provides enormous resources to greatly increase our chances of success. This chapter gives an overview of the spiritual benefits that can be ours just for the asking.

GOD'S PRESENCE

The Scriptures tell us that God's presence is with us today through the Holy Spirit. Jesus spoke very plainly about the Spirit in the Gospel of John especially.

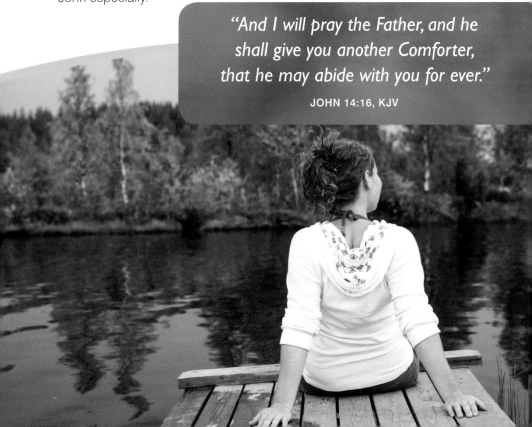

"And I will pray the Father, and he shall give you another Comforter, that he may abide with you for ever."

JOHN 14:16, KJV

The word "Comforter" is variously translated "Helper," "Advocate," Strengthener," all in an attempt to capture the breadth of assistance that the Spirit provides. Notice also the word "another" in this verse. In other words, the Holy Spirit will assist people in the same way and to the same degree that Jesus did during his earthly ministry. We were never meant to pursue our habit change journey alone.

There are several characteristics of the work of the Holy Spirit that are of particular interest to people who want to create new habits and pursue lifestyle change. The Spirit is a personal trainer and coach par excellence.

He teaches us – "But the Helper, the Holy Spirit, whom the Father will send in My name, *He will teach you all things…*" (John 14:26, NKJV, emphasis added).

I have not yet heard the Spirit speak to me audibly like a lecturer in a classroom. He usually teaches through a variety of other means such as calling our attention to Scripture, giving us impressions and thoughts, intersecting our lives with people who have the understanding or experience we need to solve our problem, calling our attention to books, articles, and websites, and putting us in certain situations to broaden our perspective.

He strengthens us – "That he would grant you, according to the riches of his glory, *to be strengthened with might by his Spirit in the inner man;* that Christ may dwell in your hearts by faith… that ye might be filled with all the fullness of God" (Ephesians 3:16-19, KJV, emphasis added).

Our inability is replaced by his ability. We are infused with vigor, persistence, and resolve.

He reveals truth – "But when he, the Spirit of truth, comes, *he will guide you into all the truth"* (John 16:13, NLT, emphasis added).

The Holy Spirit will help us see the truth about ourselves by opening our eyes to hidden biases, revealing the reality behind our excuses, and bringing conviction to our hearts. It takes a very good friend to pull us aside periodically and tell us the truth, even if we don't necessarily want to hear it. They love us enough to risk our rejection and/or wrath.

My wife and I commute to work together. I know I can count on her as the "final filter" for how I appear. The other day, as I drove down the highway, she remarked, "What on earth is that on your chin?" I glanced in the mirror and she leaned in for a closer inspection. "Ah," she said, "just a piece of breakfast," and gently wiped it away.

You can bet that no one else would have said that. They'd most likely just let me cruise through the day with a piece of unsightly, semi-burned, whole wheat toast stuck to my face. Of course, she also addresses more consequential issues in a kind, supportive way. The Holy Spirit is that same kind of caring, truth-telling Friend who'll reveal what we need to hear so that we can avoid embarrassment and be successful, happy, and fulfilled.

He gives us hope – "Now may the God of hope fill you will all joy and peace in believing, *that you may abound in hope by the power of the Holy Spirit"* (Romans 15:13, NKJV, emphasis added).

Along the path to new habit creation we may at times feel like throwing in the towel. "What's the use? I'll never make it." That's when the Spirit comes alongside, puts his arm on our shoulder, and pours hope into our hearts such as, "I know things didn't go as you wanted them to today, but you're still a fantastic person with so much talent and ability. You deserve to give yourself the gift of continuing on. You're worth it."

> *"Tomorrow's a new day, full of possibilities.*
> *Don't let today dictate your future.*
> *Simply take it one day at a time."*

GOD'S POWER

All of us have what can feel like "dead places" within us. Issues we cannot seem to overcome, failings we cannot seem to conquer. They are places where insecurity and defeat dominate.

The apostle Paul says that a special kind of heavenly power is available to Christians today for just those kinds of situations and inner needs. It is, in fact, the same life-giving power that raised Jesus from the grave:

> "I also pray that you will understand the incredible greatness of God's power for us who believe him. This is the same mighty power that raised Christ from the dead and seated him in the place of honor at God's right hand in the heavenly realms" (Ephesians 1:19-20, NLT, emphasis added).

The heavenly vitality that brought Jesus' dead body from the tomb can resurrect any of the dead places within us. All God asks is that we cooperate and surrender to his workings. The apostle reiterates the same theme again when he writes,

> "But because of his great love for us, God, who is rich in mercy, made us alive with Christ even when we were dead in transgressions – it is by grace you have been saved" (Ephesians 2:4-5, NIV, emphasis added).

Sometimes we can feel so defeated and ashamed that we are even reluctant to bring certain issues before God. But he is especially attracted to the parts of ourselves that we are most anxious to hide. He is delighted and excited to work on those places we are most embarrassed for him to explore. He has the power to make them alive.

What we view as only a history of defeat, he sees as a golden opportunity. As both Creator and Re-Creator, God is immensely skilled at turning merely existing into authentically thriving. When we focus on our failings, he focuses instead on the great potential we have in him. When we cannot imagine successful habit creation, he envisions that future as if it already exists.

The journey may well be very challenging, with missteps and setbacks. But God promises to walk by our side, keep us moving forward, and provide the resources we need to ultimately prevail. Jesus' own disciples did not change overnight. There were times when they acted badly and seemed to be going in reverse. But Jesus never retreated, never gave up on them, no matter how far they strayed from his ideal. He always had a plan, a strategy that eventually resulted in dramatic changes because they hung in there, kept following, and increasingly surrendered to his loving direction in their lives.

GOD'S PROMISES

The Scriptures are filled with promises that are a gold mine for those engaged in habit creation. Think of them as God's personal commitments to help. Here are a few pertinent verses:

"His divine power has given to us all things that pertain to life and godliness, through the knowledge of Him who called us by glory and virtue" (2 Peter 1:3, NKJV).

"Being confident of this very thing, that He who has begun a good work in you will complete it until the day of Jesus Christ" (Philippians 1:6, NKJV).

"Therefore, if anyone is in Christ, he is a new creation; old things have passed away; behold, all things have become new" (2 Corinthians 5:17, NKJV).

"Have you never heard?
Have you never understood?
The Lord is the everlasting God,
the Creator of all the earth.
He never grows weak or weary.
No one can measure the depths of his understanding.
He gives power to the weak
and strength to the powerless.
Even youths will become weak and tired,
and young men will fall in exhaustion.
But those who trust in the Lord will find new strength.
They will soar high on wings like eagles.
They will run and not grow weary.
They will walk and not faint"
(Isaiah 40:29-31, NLT).

You are not alone as you seek to develop a more abundant lifestyle. There are wonderful spiritual resources available to anyone who asks.

DISCUSSION

Are you someone who likes to "do it yourself"? If so, how might that hinder you from relying on divine resources?

....

....

How conscious are you of the work of the Holy Spirit in your life?

....

....

Is the Holy Spirit ashamed of us when we fail or do our failures make him even more anxious to help?

....

....

What do you need most right now from the Holy Spirit?

....

....

What does the phrase "dead places within us" mean for you?
How have you overcome a "dead place" in the past?

....

....

Which Bible promise in this lesson spoke to you most clearly and/or deeply? How?

....

....

Describe a time when divine resources have played an important part in your life. How can that apply to your habit development journey today?

....

....

SHARING

OPPORTUNITY #1

This section is about an opportunity for you to be a blessing to someone outside of your small group and to also deepen the impact of the lesson on your own life. The group is encouraged to discuss at the end of each meeting what aspects of the lesson they might like to share with someone at home, work, or in the community if the opportunity arises. *This page will appear at the end of each lesson and contain brief ideas of what you might pass along.*

Start each day asking God to provide opportunities to share and then keep your radar up.

You can be an ambassador and reach people with the good news that abundant living is available to all.

How this lesson can impact our Choices and Outlook

CHOICE:

1. I can invite the Holy Spirit to come more fully into my life to teach, strengthen, reveal truth, and give me hope.

2. God's resurrection power gives me the opportunity to choose new life rather than defeat and discouragement.

OUTLOOK:

1. We can be optimistic about the future knowing we do not have to face it alone.

2. The powerful promises of Scripture can be a great source of encouragement.

ABUNDANT LIVING THOUGHT

God is delighted to work on those places in our lives that we are most embarrassed for him to explore.

FAILING
SUCCESSFULLY

LESSON TWO

WARM UP

Feedback: In what ways did God open the door last week for you share some part of the lessons with someone else?

....
....
....
....

Choose one or both questions to discuss (if in group setting)
or write out your answers on a separate sheet (for individual use):

1. **What has been one of your most enjoyable, fulfilling jobs?**

....
....
....
....

2. **If you could trade job descriptions with someone at work, who would you trade with and why?**[3]

....
....
....
....

"Failing is never final unless you fail to get up!"

DR. DES CUMMINGS JR.

DISCOVERY

Imagine the following scenario. Little eleven month-old Wendy has been crawling all over the 1,800 square foot ranch house for quite some time now. Her first-time parents are eagerly awaiting the day when she'll get up from all fours and actually walk. They've dog-eared page 78 in the "Raising Baby Right" book that predicts it could happen at any time.

The signs are unmistakable. Wendy has learned to pull herself up by clutching onto the tan living room sofa. Once erect, she looks around with the satisfaction of an Olympic athlete who just won the high jump. "That's my girl," her dad encourages. The new, higher vantage point causes Wendy's face to break out in wonderment.

Then, on a cool Sunday evening at home, Wendy does her sofa routine again and her parents egg her on from across the room. "Let go, girl," her mom instructs, "you can do it. Come to mommy." She holds out her arms to bridge part of the six feet between her and their child prodigy.

The petite toddler focuses on her mother's reassuring face. Wendy turns her entire body slowly, faces mom directly, and leans forward slightly. Her parents' hearts are pounding. The wife whispers to her husband to grab the video camera, strategically prepositioned on the TV stand for this very occasion. Wendy loosens the grip of one hand. She shifts her weight, moves her pink-sneakered right foot outward, and takes a small, shaky step. She lets go with the other hand, shifts her weight again, and thrusts her left foot forward. Her parents watch breathlessly.

Then… Wendy flops down on her diapered rump. There is a moment of stunned silence. Her dad speaks up first and says indignantly, "You call that a real *attempt*?" His voice rises, "That was pathetic! We certainly expected a lot more from you at this stage."

Mom jumps in quickly, "I have to say I'm really disappointed. We've waited a long time for this moment and you choose to blow it. You know how important walking is to success in life? You obviously don't care about any of that, do you!"

Parents never react that way (I hope). When our little girl took her first brave, hesitant step before crumpling to the floor, her mother and I were her greatest cheer leaders. "Fantastic! What a great step! You did a wonderful job. We're so proud of you. We know you can do it. Keep trying."

Rather than being disappointed, we rejoiced because our daughter had just overcome a huge hurdle – *she let go*. She took the risk. Wow! That's major. Life would hold many more "letting go" experiences for her and that was the first. She had the desire because she had a vision of herself walking. Her newly minted mind had formed this daring, crayoned, stick figured goal. And with that desire and vision there would be no stopping her now. That's how supportive, caring parents interpret falling on your fanny.

That's exactly how we should interpret our own failures when trying to develop a new habit. We take a shaky first step or two or ten and then fall down. It is not unusual for our minds at that moment to shift into hyper-critical mode: *Ha! Knew you couldn't do it. You're a weak, undisciplined, unbackboned, uncommitted, unmotivated nincompoop. You might as well give up and spare yourself and others the trouble.* Our minds can be really vicious!

Instead, we need to let such words float in and then out of our minds. Notice and acknowledge them but don't dwell on them. Don't try to force them away. Don't judge them and above all don't take them seriously. We can simply shift our focus to all the words of self-encouragement we can muster: *You're getting there. You can do it. Don't let this get you down.* Concentrate on a mental image of being successful. When another discouraging thought comes, repeat the process. We need to treat ourselves as generously as parents do their wobbly, fall-prone toddlers. We may fail, but we are not failures. *We are learners.*

Jesus addressed the vital issue of fear of failure in one of his most famous stories, "The Parable of the Talents," in Matthew 25. A successful man went on a lengthy trip. Before leaving, he entrusted three of his servants with significant amounts of money. The first servant got five thousand dollars, the second two thousand, and the third one thousand. When the master returned, he asked for an accounting. The first and second servants were very entrepreneurial and had doubled the funds. The master was pleased.

He approached the third servant, "So how did things work out for *you?*"

"Oh, master," he replied, "I did really, really well. Come with me." So the servant takes him out to the backyard, carefully paces off twenty steps from the tool shed heading north, then fifteen more steps west, and begins to dig. Two feet down his shovel clunks against a square box. Hiking up his robe a little, he gets down on his knees, leans into the hole and retrieves the sturdy brown box.

After undoing the three combination locks and opening the lid, he exclaims in a self-congratulatory tone, "Here are all of the funds you lent to me. I didn't lose a single penny!"

The master is not pleased at all. "You've got to be kidding, right?" he exclaims. "At least you could have opened a Super Saver account at the Jericho Bank & Trust and earned a little interest!"

Taken aback and frightened, the servant blurts out his true inner feelings. He says, "Master, I know you have high standards and hate careless ways, that you demand the best and *make no allowances for error*" (Matthew 25:24, The Message, emphasis added). Ouch. No room for mistakes. With that perception, no wonder he buried the bucks! Fear of failure led the servant to play it safe to the extreme. He thought, "I won't gain, but I won't lose either."

That mental picture of the master was a severe distortion. The head man actually comes across as quite trusting and generous. He delegated major responsibilities, and then honored the efforts of the first two servants by giving them huge promotions. Doubling the funds in a relatively short time must have involved considerable risk, so they obviously felt the master liked to see people venture out and stretch (see Matthew 25:14-30).

The surprising truth from the parable is that it is better to have tried and failed than to have never tried at all.

The master in the Parable represents God. Jesus is teaching that our mental picture of God is vital to how we approach life. If we see God as vindictive, we will huddle deep within our comfort zones. "Not blowing it" becomes the central theme of our existence. On the other hand, if we understand that God is our greatest cheerleader, we'll focus on reaching higher, willing to fall on our backside in the pursuit of happiness and fulfillment, because we know that he is there to offer continual encouragement and support. With the assurance of heaven's partnership, we can venture out into uncharted territory in our abundant living journey.

With the assurance of heaven's partnership, we can venture out into uncharted territory in our abundant living journey.

In what I might call the Habit Creation Play, failure needs to be recast from being a villain to become one of the heroes. When it comes to habit development, failure is, in fact, key. It is a necessary and vital part of the learning process.

Generally speaking, doing something imperfectly is an inherent part of learning any new skill or ability, be it playing a musical instrument or growing carrots. Why should it be any different in personal transformation? I love the way one friend put it, "Anything worth doing is worth doing imperfectly." If you aren't messing up, you're either from another planet or you're not trying something new. Skill-building is inherently messy, full of trial and error, even for the best of us. That's why they put erasers on pencils.

Basketball legend Michael Jordan offers the following encouraging perspective, "I've missed more than 9,000 shots in my career. I've lost almost 300 games; twenty-six times I've been trusted to take the game winning shot and missed. I've failed over and over and over again in my life and that is why I succeed."[4]

IBM founder Thomas Watson Sr., got a resignation call from one of his mangers who had made a $10 million mistake. Watson refused to accept the resignation saying, "You can't be serious, we just spent $10 million educating you." Another well-known corporation will not promote someone until they've had one large public failure.[5]

We would all do well to remember the following statement from thirteenth century German theologian Meister Eckhart, "The price of inaction is far greater than the cost of making a mistake."[6]

Falling short is a very good thing if it is part of a growth process. When you fall, you never revert back to who you were. You've learned more than you might realize along the way. *Failure is a friend to be welcomed and celebrated.* Tripping up on purpose won't work, but when we do make a misstep it needs to be affirmed as potentially valuable if we react to it properly.

In order to jolt our minds away from old ways of thinking, every time we take missteps in habit creation we should shout, "Fantastic!" and throw a small personal party. Call a friend and tell them. Messing up and reacting optimistically is that important. It means you're stretching. It means you're trying. It means you understand more fully.

Hal Urban provides the following insight, "The difference between people who succeed in life and the ones who have difficulty creating success isn't found in the number of times they fail. It's found in the courage they have to take a risk, and it's found in what they do *after* they fail."[7]

When we do fail, here some key steps for "failing forward:"[8]

1. **Don't fall into self-rejection or blame.**
   Our worth doesn't come from our performance.

2. **Know that failure is only temporary.**
   The journey has both ups and downs.

3. **View failure as an isolated incident rather than generalizing that this is "the way it's *always* going to be."**

4. **Keep your expectations in line with reality.**
   Don't inflate what's doable.

5. **Re-focus on your strengths.**

6. **Make any needed adjustments in your strategy or approach.**

7. **Get going again. You only have to get up one more time than you fall down in order to be a success.**

8. **Remember that God is with you.**

John Maxwell relates the following parable on the benefits of failure that summarizes much of what this chapter is about:

> "The ceramics teacher announced on opening day that he was dividing the class into two groups. All those on the left side of the studio, he said, would be graded solely on the quantity of work they produced, all those on the right solely on its quality. His procedure was simple: on the final day of class he would bring in his bathroom scale and weigh the work of the 'quantity' group: fifty pounds of pots rated an 'A,' forty pounds a 'B,' and so on. Those being graded on 'quality,' however, needed to produce only one pot – albeit a perfect one – to get an 'A.' Well, come grading time and a curious fact emerged: the works of the highest quality were all produced by the group being graded for quantity. It seems that while the 'quantity' group was busily churning out piles of work – and learning from their mistakes – the 'quality' group had sat theorizing about perfection, and in the end had little more to show for their efforts than grandiose theories and a pile of dead clay."[9]

NOTES:

....
....
....
....
....
....
....
....
....
....
....
....
....
....
....
....
....
....
....

*We may fail,
but we are not failures.
We are learners.*

DISCUSSION

How do you feel when you see someone else's child walking unsteadily?

....

....

What advice would you give the $1,000 man in the "Parable of the Talents" to convince him not to bury the money?

....

....

In the past, have you seen God as a critic or a cheerleader? What difference can that make in how you approach life?

....

....

Tell about a time when you were really stretched in some way.

....

....

Were you raised to take risks or play it safe? What influenced you most?

....

....

When you fall down in pursuit of your new habit, what would it take to put a smile, rather than a frown, on your face?

....

....

Which of the seven key steps for "failing forward" is most meaningful for you?

....

....

Is perfectionism a problem for you? In what ways?

....

....

SHARING

OPPORTUNITY #2

- Pray as a group for God to open the way for you to share something from these lessons to help someone else this week.

- Keep your radar up each day for opportunities.

How this lesson can impact our Choices and Outlook

CHOICE:

1. Decide to view failure as another step toward success.

2. Choose now to "fail forward" utilizing the seven keys from this lesson whenever a misstep occurs.

OUTLOOK:

1. Failure is a friend to be welcomed and celebrated.

2. Failing does not make you a failure.

ABUNDANT LIVING THOUGHT

Every time we take missteps in our habit creation journey we should shout "Fantastic!" and throw a small personal party.

INSIDE YOUR BRAIN

LESSON THREE

WARM UP

Feedback: In what ways did God open the door last week for you share some part of the lessons with someone else?

....
....
....
....

Choose one or both questions to discuss (if in group setting)
or write out your answers on a separate sheet (for individual use):

1. **You are designing a float for a parade. What is the theme and how does it look?**

....
....
....

2. **How do you show love to people you care deeply about?**[10]

....
....
....

"A choice repeated often enough becomes a habit."

DR. DICK TIBBITS

DISCOVERY

Three weeks ago I found myself sitting in the emergency room waiting for a CT scan. It all started when I saw one of our office secretaries struggling to push an old typewriter stand with an old typewriter on it down the hall.

"Here, let me do that," I said.

"Are you sure?" she replied. "The wheels aren't working too well"

"Glad to do it."

She stepped back and I took over. Placing both hands on the rickety cart, I leaned into it and started to shove. Momentum built and I felt a wave of altruistic satisfaction wash over me. Suddenly the suspect wheels locked up tightly, the cart came to a quick, unexpected stop, and everything tumbled forward. I went flying over the top unable to break my fall. The left side of my forehead hit the thinly carpeted concrete floor first and scraped along for about half a foot or more. I knew I'd hit hard.

The equipment and I wound up tangled together in a painful heap next to the wall. Employees came running.

"What happened?" "Oh no!" "Are you all right?"

I hate to look weak, so I rolled over and chuckled. Then I heard someone utter the dreaded word "blood." The red stuff was pooling around three or four large scrapes. Everyone insisted I go to the local medical clinic.

"Any nausea or vomiting?" the physician inquired.

"Not yet," I uttered softly.

Then came the doc's order to report to the local hospital's emergency ward immediately for a CT scan of my rattled brain.

Three hours later I was certainly pleased with the result. The report indicated that I did, in fact, have a brain and that it was not injured. It then went on, in an almost embarrassingly complimentary way, to state:

"CEREBRUM: Cortical structures *are well formed* (emphasis added).

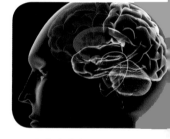

CEREBELLUM: Cerebellar hemispheres and vermis *are well formed* (emphasis added).

BRAINSTEM: Midbrain, pons, and medulla *are well formed*" (emphasis added).

To learn how "well formed" things were up there came as a delightful bonus. Such commendations have got to be extremely rare. I might even frame the report and hang it in the den.

My reaction to the hospital's report was tongue-in-cheek, but I have truly had a long time fascination with the human brain. In my research on habit development, I was especially intrigued to discover that knowing something about what's going on in our grey matter during the habit formation process can help us understand how to proceed more effectively. We can learn how certain things occur, why they occur, why we get derailed, and what actions we can take to help the brain permanently incorporate the new lifestyle choices we have made.

One of the most helpful insights regarding the brain and habit formation has to do with a substance called *myelin*. Understanding how myelin works was one of the great discoveries of recent decades. According to Dr. George Bartzokis, professor of neurology at UCLA, myelin is so fundamental that it is "the key to talking, reading, learning skills, being human."[11]

A very brief overview of brain anatomy can help get us oriented. Our brains are made up of about 100 billion nerve cells called *neurons*.[12] Each of them has the capacity to form many connections with other neurons, resulting in an extraordinary number of networks.[13]

Electrochemical signals are passed along from neuron to neuron and *are the basis for all that we think and do*. All that you have already done today, from thinking about breakfast, to getting out of bed, to driving a car, to creating a complex spreadsheet at work, was dependent on how easily millions of signals were able to travel around inside your head. That's exactly where myelin comes in. It determines both the *speed and intensity* of all those happy signals. Myelin turns mental back roads into super highways.[14]

Myelin is a white, fatty substance that acts like insulation and keeps the electrical signals in neurons from leaking out. Think of the nerve cell as a household wire and the myelin as the rubber insulation around it. Without proper wrapping, the electrical current at the end of the wire would be a lot less than what entered at the beginning. The insulation is critical. The same is true for the wiring within our brains. The insulation maintains the intensity of the signals and enables them to travel up to 100 times faster than if it was uninsulated.[15] Here is a basic diagram:

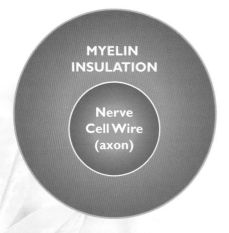

MYELIN INSULATION

Nerve Cell Wire (axon)

The bottom line is that the more myelin there is, the better the signal traveling along the neurons will be. The better the signal is, the greater our ability.

So what's all this got to do with habit formation? A lot.

The way to form new habits is to create new pathways and neural networks for signals to travel down. The gratitude journal you are starting is a new pathway. The habit of listening more and talking less is a new pathway. Taking more time for the family is a new pathway. Changing your diet, altering your attitude, walking every evening, joining a small group, and incorporating praise into your prayer life are all new pathways in your brain. The stronger those pathways, the stronger your new habit.

Myelin can make that happen. But it will only work its magic if we force those nerve cells to fire through consistent effort, *because myelin only forms if it senses electrical activity. Little effort, little myelin.*[16]

It is also important to recognize that all new pathways begin with messing up because the networks are not yet fully formed. Newborn horses can get up and walk within minutes because those particular neural networks are fully myelinated at birth. Our kids? Not so much. They get insulated later by stumbling and flopping down over and over.[17] With each attempt, the network grows a little more until one day it is formed enough and insulated enough for them to waddle five feet to mamma and eventually run. Our task is to mimic that process in the formation of new habits.

> *So struggle on. Plow ahead. Fall down and get up, over and over again. Make those nerve cells do their thing. Get those networks to grow. It is the only realistic way to success.*

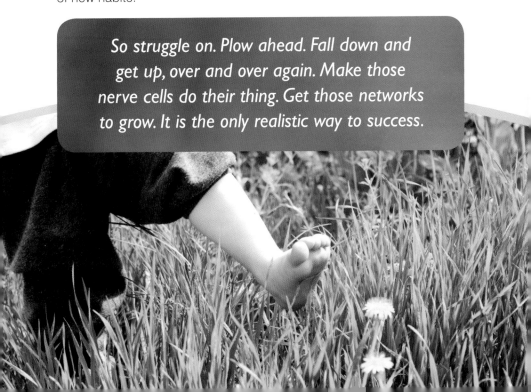

There are many Bible characters who are classic examples of stumbling toward success. One of the most beloved is the apostle Peter. He had a good heart, but started out as spiritually immature, encumbered with glaring deficiencies. His prejudice and puny people skills needed serious remodeling. His independent nature required reshaping. His impetuousness needed calming. His know-it-all perspective had to be humbled.

Jesus, of course, knew all about Peter's shortcomings before he chose him. In Christ's generous eyes, they were more than offset by Peter's tremendous potential. From day one, Jesus started coaching the burly fisherman, moving him slowly but inexorably toward greatness. Through many weeks and months of ups and downs, through victories and setbacks, Peter grew. The new habits were forming. Neural pathways were expanding. Myelin was wrapping, wrapping. Connections were being made. Eventually Peter's potential began to emerge like the first crocuses after a long winter. Over time it bloomed more and more like the panorama of floral color in a warm, rain-soaked spring.

"And do not be conformed to this world,
but be transformed by the renewing of your mind."

ROMANS 12:2, NKJV

From a habit formation perspective, it is interesting to see how Peter later recalled his lifestyle change journey over the years, remembering how he added one new habit after another, and then recommending a similar trek for others. He writes,

> *"For this very reason do your best to add goodness to your faith; to your goodness add knowledge; to your knowledge add self-control; to your self-control add endurance; to your endurance add godliness; to your godliness add Christian affection; and to your Christian affection add love" (2 Peter 1:5-7, GNT).*

Another Bible character who underwent enormous transformation was the apostle Paul. Formerly known as Saul, he used to be a very dangerous man as far as the early church was concerned. His heart had only one compelling goal – stamp out Christianity. Paul himself recounts his actions:

> *"You have been told how I used to live when I was devoted to the Jewish religion, how I persecuted without mercy the church of God and did my best to destroy it" (Galatians 1:13, GNT).*

After his conversion, Paul took considerable time off in Arabia before officially launching his public ministry as a leader in the Christian church. He needed to transition and develop new habit pathways, new ways of thinking and behaving. Former attitudes had to be overcome. Immovable perspectives needed to be moved. Interpersonal skills had to be retooled. Paul wouldn't have identified what was happening in neural network terms, but from a habit change perspective, that is exactly what needed to be done.

Looking anew at some of Paul's later writings from our modern understanding of how the brain behaves during habit formation, we can see new dimensions within old verses from the apostle's hand, such as:

> *"And do not be conformed to this world, but be transformed by the renewing of your mind" (Romans 12:2, NKJV, emphasis added).*

> *"Finally, brothers and sisters, whatever is true, whatever is noble, whatever is right, whatever is pure, whatever is lovely, whatever is admirable – if anything is excellent or praiseworthy – think about such things" (Philippians 4:8, NIV, emphasis added).*

For over twenty years my wife and I lived in Maine where friendships are strong, the scenery is gorgeous, and the winters are long, very long. As cool days approached, two topics dominated conversations – generators and insulation. "So what's the R factor of *your* insulation?" was a common inquiry. (R Factor rates the density of insulation.) I spent many hours crawling around our stifling summer attic beefing up the R factor of our primary bulwark against the inevitable cold.

When it comes to habit development, a common topic of conversation ought to be about insulation as well, the kind formed by myelin (Your M factor?). The question, "So how's *your* myelin?" would not be out of place. *Here are some keys for building great mental insulation during your habit creation journey:*

1. **Pray for God's support, guidance, and sustaining grace.**

2. **Pursue something that is beyond your reach, beyond the edges of your ability. It needs to be not so far away that you give up and not so close that you only utilize the old neural paths.**[18]

Recognize that new habits require failure. It's a biological necessity.

3. Break your new habit goal down into very small pieces and focus on one of those pieces at a time. Practice that, get it down, then move on to the next. Build up your new networks over time piece by tiny piece. If you don't seem to be making progress, break it down into even smaller tasks. As you conquer pieces, put them together into what researchers call "chunks," which then become chains like linking paper clips together.[19]

4. Target your practice, be very specific, and don't flail around. Ask, "What can I focus on today?"

5. Recognize that new habits require failure. It's a biological necessity. There is no other way to expand your thinking and lifestyle beyond the status quo. No mess, no success.[20]

6. Be patient. The time it takes is the time it takes. You cannot dictate to your neurons!

7. The more myelin you build, the more fluid and automatic each step eventually becomes.[21]

8. Old habit pathways are still around and we are especially vulnerable for the signals on our new brain pathways to "jump track" to old patterns when we are Hungry, Angry, Lonely, or Tired – HALT for short.[22]

9. Congratulate yourself for every ounce of effort.

10. Keep your eye on the prize. Don't lose track of the big picture. Don't get all tangled up in one of the bushes and lose sight of the forest. Picture yourself living that new habit. See yourself in detail walking around sporting your new lifestyle. Own it. Possess it now in your mind. Imagine the sense of accomplishment, greater happiness and health, and deeper fulfillment and satisfaction that will be yours.

Knowing the inside story of how your brain functions during habit development can give you a crucial advantage in your journey toward success.

DISCUSSION

Describe something that was once very difficult for you that you now find relatively easy to do.

....

....

How does knowing about myelin impact your attitude toward habit development?

....

....

How would you explain the role of myelin to a friend?

....

....

What are you attempting right now that is beyond your reach?

....

....

How might this lesson encourage people to stretch themselves more?

....

....

List some ways to reward yourself for small gains in habit formation?

....

....

What does it take for you to be patient with yourself?

....

....

If you called yourself a name that related to your new habit, what would it be? (For instance, Mr. Runner, Ms. Listener.)

MR./MS....

What one point was the most important for you in this lesson?

....

....

SHARING

OPPORTUNITY #3:

- Pray as a group for God to open the way for you to share something from these lessons to help someone else.

- Keep your radar up each day for opportunities.

How this lesson can impact our Choices and Outlook

CHOICE:

1. Choose to cooperate with the biological process going on in your brain during habit formation.

2. Decide to incorporate myelin building attitudes and activities into your journey.

OUTLOOK:

1. Failure is a biological necessity in learning new habits and is therefore beneficial.

2. The failures and subsequent successes of Bible characters can be a great source of encouragement.

ABUNDANT LIVING THOUGHT

Myelin creates new habit superhighways in our brain when we force nerve cells to fire through consistent effort.

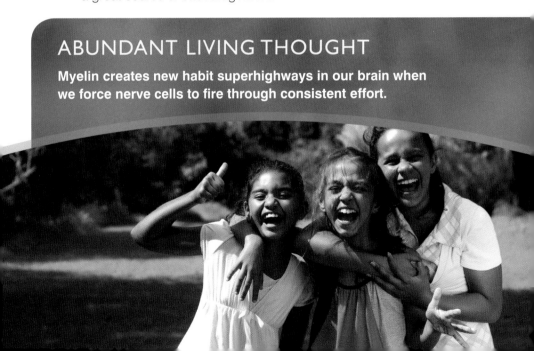

BELIEF BUSTERS

LESSON FOUR

WARM UP

Feedback: In what ways did God open the door last week for you share some part of the lessons with someone else?

....

....

....

....

Choose one or both questions to discuss (if in group setting)
or write out your answers on a separate sheet (for individual use):

1. **What do you miss the most from your childhood?**[23]

....

....

....

2. **What kinds of things stress you out the most? Explain.**[24]

....

....

....

"Outlook is your ability to stay mentally fit."

MONICA REED, MD

DISCOVERY

Much of my early childhood evenings were spent guarding against the Boogeyman. My friends and I had never actually seen one, but that simply confirmed his cleverness.

Of all the many rooms in our old family home, the Boogeyman chose to inhabit my bedroom. I would have much preferred that he took up residence in places that were more public, like the kitchen or the bathroom, but he moved in with me and I had deal with it. Another bitter unfairness, among others.

Over time, I developed a rather elaborate bedtime ritual that turned my otherwise normal looking bedroom into *Johnson's Security and Safety Headquarters.* It enabled me to survive the night without getting eaten, tortured, or carted off to the D.U.B., the "Den for Unmindful Boys."

The first area of concern was the walk-in closet, a known Boogeyman hideout. I put a coat hanger on the closet door knob with a bell on it that rang out if jiggled. I also placed various items on the floor between the closet and my bed that would make noise if inadvertently kicked. As a last resort, a baseball bat leaned against the wall within easy reach of a prone sleeping position.

The second area of concern was under the bed. Boogeymen reportedly LOVED to hang out there. Through binding agreements worked out centuries ago, the entire top of the bed was deemed safe. But anything that dangled over the edge was fair game. Heaven help you if you actually fell completely out of bed. Nerve-wracking stuff.

Where does such nonsense come from? I look back now and chuckle, but this was a powerful belief for me at the time. It impacted my youthful world view and dictated how I behaved. No empirical proof that Boogeymen existed. Just a settled belief that somehow got lodged inside my young, susceptible brain. Even to this day, I get a twinge when I wake up and find my arm dangling.

Beliefs are the precursors of all our actions. From a habit creation perspective, it is nearly impossible to form new habits without first assessing certain underlying beliefs we have about ourselves and the world around us. Actions can be changed without considering the beliefs that undergird them, but such shortcuts usually result in failure. Long-term change requires that our beliefs line up with the new lifestyle we seek to adopt.

One of the beliefs that somehow got imbedded in my brain is that, "I should make myself useful at all times." It is a simple, utilitarian message that I interpret to mean, "Don't goof off; use your time in meaningful ways." That has directly affected my choices of what to do during evenings and weekends. For instance, I sense an inner compulsion to read not about frivolous topics but about self-help programs, biographies, and history. For vacations, I prefer going to places where I can learn something new. Why on earth would anyone just sit on a beach for two weeks?

This became especially relevant when I wanted to develop a new habit of bringing more fun into my life, being more playful. That goal too often got sabotaged by the strong belief that I must be useful and constructive.

> *Long-term change requires that our beliefs line up with the new lifestyle we seek to adopt.*

Another belief that guided me for years is that I am a klutz when it comes to making things. When I try to pursue my new habit of landscaping our yard, the old belief rears its ugly head and undermines my confidence and joy.

How do such beliefs develop? Most of them originate from how we internalize our experiences and interactions over the years, especially during childhood and youth. No two people react the same way. Because we live in a sinful world, we can be the victim of negative influences that are not our fault but nonetheless impact our self-image. For instance, someone's offhand comment during the teen years that, "You'll never amount to anything," can become wired into our brain and terribly distort our self-perception. That harmful, completely inaccurate tape can play repeatedly for years until we come to believe it.[25]

In order to create sustainable habit change, *the first key* is to understand the vital role beliefs play in our lives. *The second key* is to recognize when certain beliefs are undermining our efforts to develop new habits. *The third key* is choosing to change those beliefs so they no longer hold us back.[26]

All of us have a personal belief window in front of our faces that we see everything through. Beliefs usually get on the window by default, without us proactively selecting them. So negative beliefs can get on this window as well as good ones. The great news is that we can choose what to put on the window. And as the content of the window changes, our actions change.[27]

One of the most important beliefs we need to get on to the personal belief window is belief in ourselves. Confidence that we can change and will be successful at it is fundamental.[28]

Confidence in yourself is rooted in your partnership with God and the abilities he has given you. Read the following sample Scriptures and hear God saying, "I believe in you, so why not believe in yourself?"

"What, then, shall we say in response to these things? If God is for us, who can be against us? He who did not spare his own Son, but gave him up for us all – how will he not also, along with him, graciously give us all things?" (Romans 8:31-33, NIV).

"Are not two sparrows sold for a penny? Yet not one of them will fall to the ground outside your Father's care. And even the very hairs of your head are all numbered. So don't be afraid; you are worth more than many sparrows" (Matthew 10:29-31, TNIV).

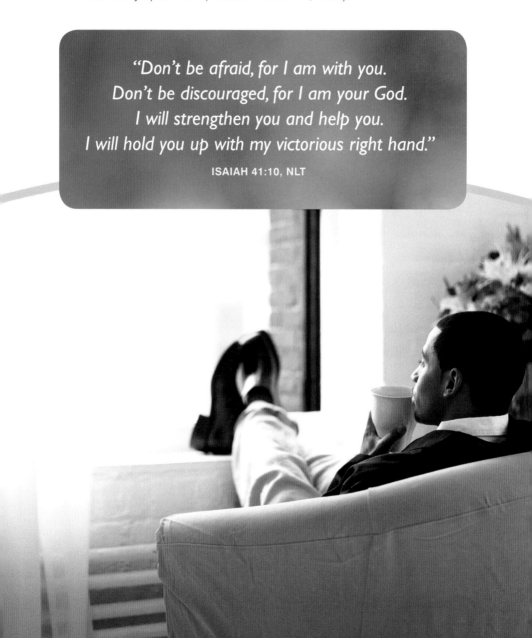

"Don't be afraid, for I am with you.
Don't be discouraged, for I am your God.
I will strengthen you and help you.
I will hold you up with my victorious right hand."

ISAIAH 41:10, NLT

Confidence in ourselves also comes from recalling past successes.[29] No matter how many stumbles or detours we have experienced, we have also had successes, big or small. Turn your attention to those and ask two questions, "What skills allowed me to accomplish what I did?" and "How can I call upon those skills now to help me move forward?"

Another underlying belief that needs examination is often referred to as the "Fixed vs. Growth Mindset."

Several years ago, researchers conducted an experiment in twelve New York City schools involving over four hundred fifth graders. One at a time, they were taken to a room and asked to solve an easy puzzle. After each one finished, they were given a short sentence of praise. Half of the children were praised for their *intelligence:* "You must be smart at this." The other half were praised for their *effort:* "You must have worked really hard."

The focus is not on getting things perfect but on learning and progressing.

They then asked the students to choose between two additional puzzles. Researchers explained that one puzzle was as easy as the one they had just taken. The other was more difficult, but they would learn a lot from it. It soon became clear that the type of praise that had been given earlier had a dramatic effect on their choices, even though it had been only one, short sentence. Ninety percent of the children who had been praised for their effort chose the harder puzzle. Most of the kids praised for their intelligence chose the easier one.

Subsequent tests were then given that were extremely difficult, designed originally for eighth graders. The praised-for-effort children dug in, got very involved, and persisted. The other children got easily discouraged and gave up.[30]

What's going on here? *The two types of praise reflect two types of mindsets.* Praising people for their *intelligence* reinforces the belief that we are all born with a certain amount of intellectual potential and that allotment remains fixed for the rest of our lives. Anything we accomplish simply reveals what is innately within us. People are smart because they were born with a certain IQ. Individuals are talented in a certain area because they are a "natural" and entered life with certain gifts. You either have it or you don't.

On the other hand, praising people for their *effort* reinforces the belief that our intelligence and talent are not determined by what endowments we are given at birth. They are not restricted to a fixed allotment. These assets can increase and grow. The mind is not static, *it is a muscle that can be developed over time.* The extent to which intelligence and talent increase depends primarily on our willingness to take on challenges, put in the effort, and expand.[31]

Fixed Mindset people are afraid to take on new challenges because they might not do well and therefore demonstrate that they are, in fact, not so smart or not so talented as they and everyone else thought. Too much is at stake. Too much is on the line. They don't want to risk looking dumb.

Conversely, Growth Mindset people don't have anything to prove. They know that if they put in the effort, they will learn new things and accomplish new things. When they falter, they simply realize that they haven't found the right strategy yet.[32] They believe in their ability to succeed if they only try. The focus is not on getting things perfect but on learning and progressing.

The truth is that we are all capable of becoming smarter and more effective. All of our minds can grow. Sociologist Benjamin Barber once said, "I don't divide the world into the weak and the strong, or the successes and the failures. I divide the world into the learners and nonlearners."[33]

The difference in the two mindsets is crucial for habit development. If we come to habit change with a Fixed Mindset, we will tend to give up when the going gets hard. We'll see any setback as an indictment of our abilities and aptitude. Alternatively, Growth Mindset people will see the habit development journey as a learning opportunity and will press through challenges with optimism and persistence.

Thankfully we were created by God with a space between thought and action, belief and behavior. We do not operate on the basis of instinct alone like reptiles that simply react to stimuli. There is a gap, a brief window of time, when we are able to consider and *choose which mindset to act on and follow. It is within this God-given time gap that new life can be found.* We can continually decide which belief system will rule.

What may hinder us from making the switch from one mindset to another is that we have lived with the old one for so long that it feels "right" and is not easy to abandon, even if it compromises our happiness and effectiveness. But even though the old version will hang around and nag, the more we select a new, life-giving outlook, the stronger it will become. You *are* able. You *can* grow. That better future is yours for the taking.[34]

A third related belief is that if something we try requires us to exert a lot of effort we must not have what it takes, we must not be built that way. We think that if people are truly gifted something should come easily. *Not true.* That is pure myth.[35]

Anders Ericsson, a pioneer in understanding how to develop expertise, has spent decades studying people in a wide cross section of fields – medicine, sports, arts, music, business, etc. His conclusion, "every expert in every field is the result of around *ten thousand hours* of committed practice."[36] For example, by the time Mozart turned age six he had already studied 3,500 hours of music with his teacher-father.[37] Michael Jordan's skill on the basketball court was more than matched by the intensity of his practice between games. No one worked harder or longer behind the scenes when the crowds weren't cheering. The great orator Winston Churchill rehearsed his speeches over and over. There are many other examples of great skill being the product of great effort.[38]

The fact that it is taking vigorous effort to reach your habit development goal is no reflection on either your ability or the likelihood of achieving success. The only legitimate conclusion to draw from your struggles is that you are a committed, growth-oriented person who has the courage to reach significantly beyond what is easy and familiar.

> *You are able. You can grow.*
> *That better future is yours for the taking.*

DISCUSSION

Do you have a Boogeyman type story from your childhood?

....

....

What are some false beliefs you carried into adulthood that have affected your behavior?

....

....

In what areas of your life is your self-confidence the strongest? The weakest?

....

....

What increases your self-confidence?

....

....

Were you raised with a Fixed or Growth mindset? How can you tell? Give examples.

....

....

How do you react when faced with a hard task? Are you eager or fearful?

....

....

What conclusions do you draw when a task comes easily to someone? Is that an accurate assessment?

....

....

What difference does it make in your thinking to divide the world up into "learners" and "non-learners" rather than successes and failures?

....

....

SHARING

OPPORTUNITY #4:

- Pray as a group for God to open the way for you to share something from these lessons to help someone else.

- Keep your radar up each day for opportunities.

How this lesson can impact our Choices and Outlook

CHOICE:

1. We can choose what beliefs to put in our personal belief window.

2. Adopting a Growth Mindset is essential for successful habit formation.

OUTLOOK:

1. Self-confidence primarily comes from trusting God's evaluation of us.

2. A key to progress is viewing ourselves as learners.

ABUNDANT LIVING THOUGHT

"I divide the world into the learners and nonlearners."
BENJAMIN BARBER

HANDLING
THE HECKLER

LESSON FIVE

WARM UP

Feedback: In what ways did God open the door last week for you share some part of the lessons with someone else?

....

....

....

....

Choose one or both questions to discuss (if in group setting)
or write out your answers on a separate sheet (for individual use):

1. **Who has been one of your most unusual neighbors?**[39]

....

....

....

2. **What is a habit you're glad to have?**[40]

....

....

....

"What we call the secret of happiness is no more a secret than our willingness to choose life."

LEO BUSCAGLIA

DISCOVERY

The skies were darkening on the horizon of John the Baptist's life. Arrested and imprisoned by King Herod, John, who had lived outdoors for so many years, now languished in a small, dreary cell, cut off from all that was familiar. No longer able to preach. No prospect of release.

After weeks of suffering, a foreboding voice began to assert itself within his head. At first a whisper and then a drumbeat, it raised the unthinkable question, "Was Jesus really the Messiah?" Up until that point, John had felt such strong assurance, such invincible faith. His mind was convinced that Jesus was the Anointed One.

But now the Baptist struggled. "If he *is* the Messiah," the voice insisted, "why hasn't he delivered you?" John tried to push such thoughts away, but they only grew stronger. "You're life has been a waste," it mocked. "All that preparation, all that sacrifice. How could you imagine that a Carpenter from Nazareth was the Expected One. Nothing but a mirage." The voice was sucking the life and optimism out of the jailed man's heart.

> *One of the biggest determiners of whether or not you will be successful in your habit creation journey is how you relate to those voices within.*

Eventually John had to find out if the question was true, so he sent emissaries to ask Jesus directly. Christ simply pointed to the miraculous works he was doing every day as a clear indication he was divine. It was enough to renew John's faith and put his thinking back on track (see Matthew 11:1-6).

Here was the person of whom Jesus declared, "I tell you the truth, of all who have ever lived, none is greater than John the Baptist" (Matthew 11:11, NLT). And yet even John had to wrestle with two opposing voices that were engaged in a tug of war within his mind – one life-giving, the other life-sapping. John's habit of focusing people's attention on Jesus was imperiled by this inner strife.

His mental struggle was not unique. The subject matter changes, but the presence of competing voices within our brains is universal. The topic varies, but the dueling voices within each of us remain. For John it was the role of Jesus, for us it can be any topic whatsoever, any subject or focus. No one is immune.

One of the biggest determiners of whether or not you will be successful in your habit creation journey is how you relate to those voices within. I'm not speaking of the kinds of "voices" that plague those unfortunate souls suffering from severe mental illness. I'm talking about the garden variety voices that speak to us as thoughts throughout the day.

There are two main characters. One is the beneficial Life-Coach Voice that guides, encourages, teaches, and holds us lovingly accountable. The other is the bad Heckler Voice that sits up there in your cranium 24/7 making negative pronouncements on your life. It is this latter voice that is most dangerous to your habit creation efforts.

Think of the worst boss you've ever had. *That's* the kind of voice I'm talking about. At least we can escape the awful boss at the end of the workday, but the Heckler has taken up residence in our brain and cannot be evicted. The thoughts it generates are automatic and cannot be shut off, *but they can be managed and overcome.*

The Heckler's influence and impact can be more pronounced in some people than in others, but unless we know how to deal with him, we'll most likely stumble badly and possibly even fail in our attempt to develop abundant living habits. Knowing how to handle his lies is crucial to success.

The Heckler's negative pronouncements can come in various forms. There is, for instance:[41]

- **The voice of judgment.** It likes to shame, blame, undermine, condemn, and harass. The Heckler knows how to sap our confidence and optimism. It knows how to kick us when we're down. There is no allowance for circumstances. It is like a car insurance policy where we are always at fault, no matter what the facts may be.

- **The voice of exaggeration.** A bump in the road becomes a "disaster." A slight stumble becomes a "mess." A minor detour becomes a "calamity."

- **The voice of self-deprecation.** Some of its favorite words are loser, fraud, hypocrite, and weakling.

- **The voice of skepticism.** "There is no way that's going to work." "Who are you kidding?" "You'll never recover from that relapse." "You have no self-control." "You've failed before and you'll fail again."

- **The voice of fear.** "It's only a matter of time before you embarrass yourself," "What if…"

- **The voice of distortion.** "That habit goal you chose is way too big and difficult."

The Heckler sounds so insistent and confident that we tend to believe him. He is with us so consistently that we get used to him and think his perspective is normal and must be the truth. The more we believe his lies, the more tentative we become. Change suffers. Our lives get more restricted and measured in order to avoid his wrath. We give up more readily.

So what can be done? If we can't get rid of the Heckler, how can we deal with him? How can we clip his wings and handle his pronouncements? *The following are some keys to keeping the Heckler in line.*

1. Awareness.

Simply being aware of who the Heckler is and what he is up to is a big step forward. Too often people get caught up in his storyline and neglect to step back out of the story and become a spectator.

Rather than taking what he says as gospel, become an observer and say to yourself, "Oh, here he goes again. What is he going to dump on me today? What distortions is he going to tell?"

The point is to create space between what the Heckler says and how you choose to respond. Take a few deep breaths, walk around the block. It also helps to write down some of his most annoying, debilitating thoughts so you can examine them more objectively. Doing so also helps you recognize that thought when it comes around again so you can be more proactive and deal with it earlier. Observe, assess, but don't believe.[42]

The point is to create space between what the Heckler says and how you choose to respond. Take a few deep breaths, walk around the block.

2. Understanding.

The Heckler came into existence when you were a child and developed over time. At first he was the composite of all the voices in your young life that were trying to *protect you from shame and pain.* It included parents, teachers, classmates, pastors, police, coaches, store managers, clerks, principals, janitors, bosses, friends, etc. A wide amalgam of personalities, all with good motives and intentions, gave you admonishments, criticisms, and warnings. The Heckler chose what to retain and what to ignore. Unfortunately, your mind is like Velcro to critical comments and Teflon to complimentary ones. So the Heckler gave negative statements almost exclusive priority.

Over the years, as your world got much bigger and your responsibilities dramatically increased, the Heckler saw dangers on every hand. He took the words from earlier years, pumped them up and morphed them from calm advice into shouts of hyper-critical vigilance. As he looked out on society, he saw threats everywhere and overreacted. As hurtful as the Heckler's voice can be, it stems from good motives that, unfortunately, too often go amuck.[43] What happens is reminiscent of *auto-immune disease* where the body's immune system that was originally designed to protect us makes a mistake and begins to attack us instead.[44]

Add to that mix all of the mean, nasty, demeaning things ill-intentioned people say to us along the way and the Heckler has plenty of fodder for his assaults.

3. Interruption.

When you recognize the Heckler's voice for what it is, find some word or phrase to stop him in his tracks before he can ramble on ad nauseam. Something simple like, "Wait a minute!" "Stop!" "That's enough!" "That's not right!" "Hold on there buster!" It doesn't make him go away, but it halts the litany and puts you on alert. It's like hitting the reset button on your computer.[45]

4. Stating the truth.

Because you have been listening to the Heckler for so long, it may be hard at first to speak up in opposition. His voice has gained undeserved credibility over the years, but now you know better. Researchers have discovered that the more we resist negative thoughts directly the stronger they become. (Like trying to *not* think about the white monkey.) So don't get into a debate with the Heckler. He is tricky and has numerous come backs. Simply state your truth for your own benefit, repeat it as often as you need to, choose to believe that truth, and then move on.[46]

No matter how loud and insistent the Heckler's voice seems, it will rise in a crescendo and then fade. The sooner you deal with it the better, but that episode will eventually quiet down on its own.

5. Positive replacement.

Rather than ceding brain territory to the Heckler by default, take back that space by filling it with positive, encouraging thoughts during times of relative quiet. The stronger and more prevalent these thoughts are, the easier it will be to recall them when a Heckler attack occurs.

Develop affirmations about yourself. Put them on 3x5 cards and keep them in your purse or pocket. Scripture is a great source, as well as inspirational stories about the habit change journeys of others. Positive replacement is like switching the channel on your car radio. It is up to you to come up with the content for that alternate channel or else there'll be nothing to switch to in time of need.

6. Compassion for ourselves.

The very best way to deal with headwinds of negativity is to develop an attitude of compassion *toward ourselves.* Imagine you have a friend who is accepting, kind, compassionate, and unfailingly supportive. This friend is a great listener and always available. *That is the type of person you need to be for yourself.* When you are under pressure from the Heckler, when you struggle and stumble, relate to yourself in the same way your wonderful friend would.

For instance, when you fail, focus much more on the feelings of disappointment that are present rather than on the failure itself. When you come up short, focus much more on the let down you feel, rather than on the shortfall. Bring comfort and solace to your own heart - "I know you're hurting, but you will do better next time. I believe in you." Author Kristin Neff writes that whenever something goes wrong in her life, she silently repeats the following comforting phrase:

> *This is a moment of suffering.*
> *Suffering is part of life.*
> *May I be kind to myself in this moment.*
> *May I give myself the compassion I need.*[47]

The very best way to deal with headwinds of negativity is to develop an attitude of compassion toward ourselves.

We all grow best in an atmosphere of nurture rather than criticism. We feel free to become who we long to be when we do not fear rejection. We feel free to be creative when we know we won't be ridiculed. We feel free to open up to the future when we don't have to worry about being condemned. Those freedoms can be ours if we express our deepest compassion and nurturance toward ourselves. It gives us a ready-made safety net and refuge. It creates a bulwark against the barbs and negativity of others. It provides an additional layer of insulation from words that drain our energy and optimism.

Another label we could give this concept is self-kindness:

> *"[Self-kindness] means we allow ourselves to be emotionally moved by our own pain, stopping to say, 'This is really difficult right now. How can I care for and comfort myself in this moment?' With self-kindness, we soothe and calm our troubled minds. We make a peace offering of warmth, gentleness, and sympathy from ourselves to ourselves, so that true healing can occur."*[48]

Like a good friend, listen carefully to your own needs and speak words of encouragement to your own heart in response.

Jesus told us plainly, "Love your neighbor *as yourself*" (Matthew 22:39, NLT, emphasis added). The "as yourself" section too often gets lesser billing, but it is an integral part of the commandment. It means that we should shower ourselves with as much love, kindness, and understanding as we are expected to share with others.

The Scriptures also tell us, "But God demonstrates His own love toward us, *in that while we were still sinners, Christ died for us*" (Romans 5:8, NKJV, emphasis added). "While we were still sinners" means that at the time Jesus chose to be nailed to a cross, humanity was still rebelling, blowing it, messing up. His choice to sacrifice himself anyway is called grace. Loving the unlovely. It is that example of God's graciousness toward us that we need to exhibit toward ourselves. It includes forgiving ourselves as well.

Such an attitude of self-care can serve to counter the Heckler and provide the right antidote for his toxic words. It is the soil within which our new habit creation can thrive and grow.

Hopefully this lesson will help keep us from being derailed, distracted, or discouraged by the false messages that can come our way as we journey toward habit formation success.

DISCUSSION

How can you tell the difference between the Life Coach voice and the Heckler voice inside your head?

....
....

What are some of your Heckler's favorite things to say?

....
....

In what situations and circumstances does the Heckler have the most influence on you?

....
....

What does it mean to you to "step outside yourself and become an observer"?

....
....

Do you battle negative thoughts or simply observe them? What helps you the most to get rid of them?

....
....

Describe your reaction to Kristin Neff's phrase. What meaning does it have for you?

....
....

What would change in your life if you started practicing "self-kindness" regularly?

....
....

What words of compassion could you say to yourself when you are hurting? How about when you feel like giving up your new habit pursuit?

....
....

SHARING

OPPORTUNITY #5:

- Pray as a group for God to open the way for you to share something from these lessons to help someone else.

- Keep your radar up each day for opportunities.

How this lesson can impact our Choices and Outlook

CHOICE:

1. The Heckler voice does not have to dictate our choices.

2. We can choose how to keep the Heckler in line.

OUTLOOK:

1. The Heckler's pronouncements are not the truth about who we are.

2. We are worthy of our own compassion.

ABUNDANT LIVING THOUGHT

When you recognize the Heckler's voice for what it is, say, "Stop! That's enough!"

LEARNING TO SAY "NO"

LESSON SIX

WARM UP

Feedback: In what ways did God open the door last week for you share some part of the lessons with someone else?

....

....

....

....

Choose one or both questions to discuss (if in group setting)
or write out your answers on a separate sheet (for individual use):

1. **Did you have a secret hideout as a child? Describe.**[49]

....

....

....

2. **If you could eliminate one weakness or limitation in your life, what would it be?**[50]

....

....

....

*"We all find time
to do what we really
want to do."*

WILLIAM FEATHER

DISCOVERY

What would you say is the most amazing two letter word in the English language? I'd vote with both hands for the word "no." I don't use it often enough, but whenever I do it helps me to:

- maintain balance in my life

- experience less stress

- sleep better at night

- refrain from cramming my mouth with comfort food.

I don't know who originally thought of putting those two letters together, but they are certainly a powerful, under-valued, combination. There are gazillions of two letter combinations such as AT, OF, IT, BE, GO, HI, SO, TO, WE, etc. But, for peace of mind and balanced living, nothing holds a candle to NO.

When I was a young pastor, someone invited me to speak for the annual week of spiritual emphasis at a school about six hours north by car. After I hung up the phone, I thought, "Man, I've made the speaking circuit!" Unbridled pride welled up within my self-absorbed soul. The assignment involved four talks each day covering grades 1-4, 5-6, 7-8, and finally 9-12.

After extensive preparation, I arrived at the school on Monday morning to watch the buses unload. As the kids poured off, shouting and shoving, I began to have second thoughts. "How on earth am I going to hold the attention of all these different age groups?" My stomach decided to express its own misgivings. I ran inside to the boys' bathroom and promptly lost every last bite of a delicious breakfast. The speaking circuit suddenly didn't look so glamorous any more.

Friday afternoon, on the way home, I concluded that it's fun and exhilarating to accept speaking appointments, but the problem is that *you actually have to go there and do it!* Bummer. For my melancholy innards it's awfully nerve-wracking. Eventually I learned that all I had to do was say the magic word, "no." Sure, my people-pleaser side scolds for a minute or two, but it soon quiets down.

Knowing when to say "no" presumes that we understand ourselves and what fits our personality, energy level, and priorities. Otherwise we are susceptible to pressure and manipulation.

No one faced more manipulation and pressure than Jesus. Nonetheless, he kept his priorities together. At the end of his life, Christ inserted a very telling phrase into his famous prayer in John 17. In verse 4, Jesus said to his heavenly Father, "I have finished the work *which You have given Me to do*" (John 17:4, NKJV, emphasis added). He didn't finish the work that the Pharisees gave him to do. He didn't finish the work that his followers gave him to do. He didn't finish the work that his own mother gave him to do. The Savior did what he sensed God the Father wanted done each day and that must have taken a donkey cart load of "no's." It didn't make him popular with some segments of society, but it kept him on track for his life's mission.

The prophet Daniel in the Old Testament is another stellar example of saying "no" in order to preserve one's principles and preferred direction in life. Traipsed off as a young man by the enemy to the far away city of Babylon in 605 B.C., he and his companions were subjected to training for royal service.

Daniel's first major "no" was his refusal to eat his captor's offer of artery clogging foods and brain-cell destroying drink. The Bible records, "At the end of the ten days they [Daniel and his friends] looked better and more robust than all the others who had been eating from the royal menu" (Daniel 1:15, The Message).

Another major "no" came when Daniel's jealous opponents tricked the new king, Darius the Median, into signing the following decree: "For the next thirty days no one is to pray to any god or mortal except you, O king. Anyone who disobeys will be thrown into the lions' den" (Daniel 6:7, The Message). The problem was that for many years Daniel had followed the habit of praying to God three times every day.

The choice: pray to God and get eaten by lions or comply. He chose to pray heavenward. Talk about sticking with your priorities! The result? After a night confined with the beasts, Daniel declared, "My God sent His angel and shut the lions' mouths, so that they have not hurt me" (Daniel 6:22, NKJV).

The prophet's "no's" spanned the gamut from the dinner plate to the den of lions and I'm sure there were many unrecorded "no's" in between, both big and small.

In order to get you to accede to their desires, people will often try to make you feel either ignorant, anxious, or guilty.

Learning to say "no" is critical because if we are going to insert a new habit into our current lifestyle, we're going to have to make room for it by saying "no" to something else. Simply adding it on will usually prove unworkable because it gets quickly crowded out when it has to compete with tasks and routines that are already an established part of our life. After you have done the important work of understanding your values, resetting your priorities, developing an Abundant Living Action Plan (lesson #8), and creating specific lifestyle goals, all of that effort can get sabotaged if you are not able to preserve and protect them by saying "no" when necessary.

As author Mark Weinstein observes, "Being powerful in saying 'No' is as important as being powerful in saying 'Yes.'"[51]

Several years ago I discovered that there are three ways that people try to manipulate others into saying "yes" to their requests. Being able to recognize these manipulative strategies can help you avoid becoming a victim. In order to get you to accede to their desires, people will often try to make you feel either *ignorant, anxious, or guilty.*

- *Ignorant:* "If you only understood the need," "If you had my background and experience, you'd understand why this is important," etc.

- *Anxious:* "If you don't do this then…," "No one does it like you do," etc.

- *Guilty:* "Everyone is counting on you," "It won't be the same without you," etc.

These requests may come from well-meaning people, but they can be deadly to your own best choices. Manipulation from whatever motive is never an appropriate way to get others to take certain actions. You have the freedom to be true to your own values and priorities. You have the freedom to choose what fits best into your life direction and personal needs. Giving in to someone else's manipulation only opens the door to resentment and regret.

Saying "no" when necessary also depends on your ability to distinguish between what is *urgent* and what is truly *important*. Urgent things are those that come at us labeled "right now" or "as soon as possible or sooner." They are insistent, adamant, and inflexible. Important things are those that line up with our *predetermined* values and priorities. The key word here is "predetermined." Unless you know your own values and priorities ahead of time, you will likely be subject to others' whims and anxiety.[52]

By way of analogy, think of a glass jar with several large rocks and a pile of pebbles on the side. The rocks are our priorities and the pebbles are the list of urgent tasks others press upon us. If we put the pebbles in first, there will not be room for all of the rocks, which means frustration. The key is to put the large rocks in *first* and then fit as many of the pebbles in as possible.[53]

In my former life as a pastor, the phone used to ring off the hook with urgent requests. What I considered to be more important tasks often got crowded out. Finally I learned to write into my schedule big rock things like study time, family time, exercise, recreation, a day off, and so forth *before the next week started*, before the pebbles showed up. Even then, I struggled and gave in too often. Two additional insights helped: (1) treat my own big rocks as more important than other people's requests (unless it was a true emergency); (2) stop feeling like I had to justify and explain my choices.

Author M. J. Ryan quotes the following story from a very busy executive who used to find it impossible to add exercise to his hectic schedule:

> *"But then someone asked me to think of an occasion when in the midst of a busy work life I'd taken time for what mattered to me. Instantly the birth of my son came to mind. Despite flying around the country, I was there at his birth and for almost every dinnertime for the following eight years. I could do it because I vowed that the company was not going to take my family time. When I thought about this in connection with exercising, I realized that I was part of my family too and if I didn't take care of myself, I was cheating them."*[54]

Saying "no" takes determination. We find it hard to do because we are people pleasers, genuinely want to help, fear being thought rude, hope to avoid conflict, or don't want to burn bridges. In most cases, saying "no" doesn't evoke any of these negative results. *Most of the time the key is knowing how.*

Celestine Chua gives us seven ways to say "no" kindly but firmly:[55]

1. **"I can't commit to this as I have other priorities at the moment." If you place those priorities in your appointment calendar months ahead of time, you can tell people that those dates are already taken without having to explain why.**

2. **"Now's not a good time as I'm in the middle of something. How about we reconnect at X time?"**

3. **"I'd love to do this, but…"**

4. **"Let me think about it first and I'll get back to you." Let them know when to expect a reply.**

5. **"This doesn't meet my needs now, but I'll be sure to keep you in mind."**

6. **"I'm not really the best person to help on this. Why don't you try X?"**

7. **"No, I'm sorry, but I can't."**

The ability to say "no" is a vital element in achieving success in all your habit creation endeavors.

DISCUSSION

On a scale of 1 to 10, how hard is it for you to say "no" where 1 is very easy and 10 is very hard?

. . . .

. . . .

Is it easier for you to say "no" in certain situations than it is in others? To certain people than it is to others?

. . . .

. . . .

How do you think Jesus was able to say "no" so effectively? What can we learn from him?

. . . .

. . . .

If people try to manipulate you into doing something by making you feel ignorant, anxious, or guilty, should you always refuse or sometimes give in? How do you decide?

. . . .

. . . .

What is one of the hardest "no's" you have ever had to say?

. . . .

. . . .

What would it take for you to keep the big rocks in place and not cave in to pressure?

. . . .

. . . .

How many of the seven ways to say "no" would you feel comfortable using? Why? Give an example of how you might use one of them.

. . . .

. . . .

SHARING

OPPORTUNITY #6:

- Pray as a group for God to open the way for you to share something from these lessons to help someone else.

- Keep your radar up each day for opportunities.

How this lesson can impact our Choices and Outlook

CHOICE:

1. We can choose to make room for our new habit by using the word "no" more effectively.

2. Incorporating a new habit into our lives will involve avoiding manipulation by others and maintaining our assertiveness rights.

OUTLOOK:

1. Saying "no" appropriately helps us avoid feelings of resentment, guilt, and anxiety.

2. We can use the word "no" with confidence and peace of mind when we know how.

ABUNDANT LIVING THOUGHT

If we are going to insert a new habit into our current lifestyle we have to say "no" to something else.

HARNESS YOUR FULL MIND

LESSON SEVEN

WARM UP

Feedback: In what ways did God open the door last week for you share some part of the lessons with someone else?

....
....
....

Choose one or both questions to discuss (if in group setting)
or write out your answers on a separate sheet (for individual use):

1. **What song makes you instantly happy?**[56]

....
....
....
....

2. **What's your favorite subject to discuss? Why?**[57]

....
....
....
....

> *"Hope is the most powerful stimulant for the body."*
>
> **JOHN HARVEY KELLOGG, MD**

DISCOVERY

A man named Elliot entered the office of neurologist Antonio Damisio in 1982 with a stunning problem. He couldn't make decisions, at least not without incredible difficulty. Because of a tumor, surgeons had previously removed the part of his brain that accessed feelings. Tumor free, Elliot had hoped to renew his happy family life, return to his important job in a large corporation, and re-engage with his local church. But that now seemed impossible.

Everyday choices such as which color pen to use or which radio station to listen to became subjects of endless analysis. He tried to decide where to eat lunch by visiting several restaurants and poring over menus, comparing their seating plans, lighting, and other amenities. Overwhelmed by all the variables, he could not come to a conclusion. Trying to make an appointment to see someone took hours. He scanned his appointment book endlessly, considering the cost-benefit of every potentiality. The process was both bewildering and utterly exhausting.

Eventually, as a result of his pathological struggles, Elliot lost his job and family, then sunk into financial ruin. The neurologist he sought out for help, Dr. Damasio, took on the challenge and began a lengthy period of analysis. What could have happened?

One of the biggest clues was Elliot's lack of emotion. Damisio observed that he was completely dispassionate about his current difficulties. He also evaluated Elliot's emotional responses scientifically by showing him various dramatic pictures while hooked up to a machine that measures the output of the sweat glands. No response. As a result of the required surgery, Elliot had the emotional capacity of a robot.[58]

This became part of a new understanding by researchers like Damisio regarding the vital role feelings play in decision making. It was new territory for scientists and ran counter to centuries of consensus on how the brain actually worked.

It had been understood for a long time that we are, essentially, double minded. We have a *rational brain*, called the frontal cortex, and an *emotional brain*, called the limbic system.

In order to avoid repeating the words "rational brain" and "emotional brain" over and over, I'm going to take the liberty of giving them abbreviations.

- The *rational brain* we'll call *"RB."*

- The *emotional brain* we'll call *"EB."*

Let's go a step further and think of them as siblings, two members of the same family.

For centuries, people thought of EB as the source of "animal passions," full of base urges, impulsive, undisciplined, impetuous. RB on the other hand, was cool, steady, thoughtful. The consensus was that wild EB needed to be corralled and suppressed by wise RB. The ideal of humanity was for reason to consistently trump feeling. Plato, Descartes, Freud, and many other thought leaders promulgated this philosophy down through history and it was eventually adopted by Western culture. It still pervades modern society today.[59]

The problem is that it's wrong. And that misunderstanding has had a very detrimental effect on people's approach to habit development.

Scientists have discovered that in order to make good decisions we need BOTH aspects of our brain; we need both RB and EB working *together.* One is not primitive and the other of a higher level; they have an equally important role to play. *They need each other and both need to be consulted.* That is why when the part of Elliot's brain that was responsible for plugging into his feelings was removed, he was adrift. The rational brain tried to make it solo but became dysfunctional and neurotic trying.[60]

RB and EB assimilate information from facts, data, and life experiences into different parts of our mind. After considering the information, both then report to us in different ways. RB gives us the analysis, the numbers, the tally sheet, the pros and cons *through conscious thought.* EB, on the other hand, gives us a *feeling*, an intuition, a gut reaction, positive or negative, designed to steer us in a certain direction.[61] Sometimes they are in sync, telling the same story, pointing in the same direction. Other times they disagree. In fact, they disagree quite often.[62]

So we need to listen to *both*, and when they disagree, go with one or the other.

My wife and I called upon both RB and EB when we purchased our home in Florida. We both are very skittish about spending, so we took several months to look around. We wore out one real estate agent after saying "no" to thirty houses. Our second agent led us to the house we now occupy within a couple of days. After we had toured all of the rooms, the agent said, "The market is starting to go crazy, and if you wait to decide, someone else will get it. You have to decide *now*."

Well, our inner RB didn't like that one single bit. He already had tons of information, but desperately wanted more. Thankfully EB stepped in. My wife and I agreed that the home just "felt right." So we signed and have been happy ever since. Without EB at that moment, we'd have been stuck somewhat like poor Elliot we talked about earlier who couldn't decide anything. We didn't purchase on a whim. But it was time to move ahead and only EB could deliver us from the "paralysis of analysis."

> *My wife and I agreed that the home just "felt right." So we signed and have been happy ever since.*

When it comes to habit creation, we need both RB and EB as well. Once we understand how they basically function, we can accommodate their needs as much as possible and reject their insistent voices when either over-reaches or over-reacts. We can listen to both, consult with both, and make choices in a more balanced, effective way. There are several key habit development issues that harnessing our full mind can help address.

1. Lack of clarity.

Because of his love of analysis, RB gets very nervous when our habit goals lack clarity. He wakes us up in the middle of the night and inquires, "Where on earth are you taking me?" He needs specifics. He wants to see the details. It helps RB a lot when we write out our goals and say, "There, see that, does that make you happy now?" It also helps to practice mentally visualizing your habit creation goal. The more RB can picture it, the more satisfied and accepting he will be.[63] Our old habits are usually on automatic. We do them without thinking. If our new habit goals are unclear, RB will shove us back to the familiar, the old status quo, the last place he felt comfortable.

2. Too much information.

If we try to look at change from every conceivable angle before we act, RB will feel swamped with facts and rebel. The more information RB has, the more potential problems his analytic mind sees. The more choices he has to sort out, the more exhausted he gets.[64] This means that we need to do a reasonable amount of inquiry, but not insist on getting a PhD in the topic before moving ahead. Taking some time to let the facts sink in is also helpful for RB. If we make him feel like we just inserted an information firehose into his mouth, he won't be a happy camper.

3. Depending too much on willpower.

Depending on willpower alone means depending on RB to do all the heavy habit change lifting. It depends on RB repeatedly saying, "I know this is good for me so I'll force myself to stick it out," "I've gotta do this," or "The evidence is clear; I have to make this happen."

The problem is that willpower is an exhaustible resource. It is often the case that people are unable to sustain change simply because their mental muscles are worn out. They aren't "weak willed" and they don't "lack backbone." They have simply not learned how to utilize both parts of their brain. They are imbalanced in their attempt, relying on RB alone.[65]

It is from EB that we get the primary energy and motivation to keep going. Facts alone don't usually provide the impetus to make things happen. We need to go back to EB again and again for the inspiration to persevere, sometimes on a daily or even hourly basis. We also need to take time to feed EB and keep him pumped up. Reading/hearing success stories from others can help immensely. That's why so many lifestyle change websites contain stories about improvements people made. Inspirational quotes are also valuable. Martin Luther King Jr's "I Have Dream" speech never fails to get my juices flowing when I hear it. That's EB.

4. Not enough fun.

EB is a fun loving guy. If he perceives our habit development goal as being utterly BORING, he won't engage. He'll sit on the sidelines with his chin in his hands and pout. No matter how serious the new habit issue may be, we have to find some way to make it appealing and enjoyable or else EB will bow out and leave us in the lurch. Motivation will dry up.[66] Look for "bright spots" to celebrate as often as possible to keep EB happy.

5. Too risky.

EB is also about feeling safe. If he thinks our new habit will cause us to fall flat on our face, he'll put on the brakes. He does not want to feel embarrassed. We overcome that by helping him understand that failure in this case is GOOD because it means we are stretching and growing. It is a source of pride, not shame. Failure is a requirement if we are ever to get outside our comfort zones and find deeper levels of fulfillment, health, and satisfaction in life.

6. EB has gotten too big.

There are many times when RB doesn't have a chance because EB is so much stronger in a certain area. It's like me arm wrestling a professional weight lifter. We have followed EB's lead so often in the past that he has built up bulging emotional muscles. In this case, we have to tweak our environment to give RB a fighting chance. The key is to put in place processes and mechanisms that boost RB's influence. We do that *before* EB is engaged. For example:

- Put your alarm clock across the other side of the bedroom when you go to bed at night so you have to get up and walk over to turn it off in the morning. Otherwise, as soon as your eyes blink open, EB will be shouting, "Stay right here. It's ssoooo comfy and warm under these blankets. Another thirty minutes won't make any difference whatsoever." And before RB has even had a chance to get oriented, EB has won the battle. Walking across the room gives RB time to have his say.

- Freeze your credit cards in a cube of ice (or even better, throw them away). Ads, commercials, and displays are typically designed to grab EB and bypass RB. When you are in the store and see that fantastic household item on sale, EB will be jumping up and down saying, "Love it! Really love it! Gotta have it right now!" If your credit card is handy, EB will win. Having to thaw the little critters out first gives RB time to kick in and make his arguments, such as, "You can't afford it!"

- Getting temptations out of the house so you have to physically drive to get them also gives RB a fighting chance to make his points before EB drowns him out.

7. Short-term is more appealing.

RB is usually the one who is attracted to long-term goals. EB, on the other hand, is much more likely to opt for immediate satisfaction. To overcome that imbalance, you have to break long-term goals into much smaller ones that will get EB on board.[67]

8. Putting ourselves into either/or situations.

For habit creation to be successful, we need to avoid pathways that pit RB against EB. Optimal change occurs when we strategize to get them working together so that RB has clarity and EB is motivated. RB provides the map and EB gives the energy.[68]

Jesus kept RB and EB in wonderful balance all during his life, harnessing the full power of both. The only time we see them in conflict is in the Garden of Gethsemane at the end of his life. It is a glaring example of how these two mental siblings can vie for attention, even within the mind of Christ.

When he arrived in the Garden he exclaimed, "My soul is overwhelmed with sorrow to the point of death" (Matthew 26:38, NIV). Then Jesus fell to the ground and cried out three times with mind-boggling depth of emotion, "Father, if there is any other way than the cross and separation from you, please find it" (Matthew 26:42, paraphrase). His emotional mind recoiled at what lay ahead and screamed at him to avoid it. Eventually, however, the rational mind carried the day and he went forth to Calvary. What an incredible decision!

NOTES:

....
....
....
....
....
....
....
....
....
....
....
....
....
....
....
....
....
....
....
....

It is often the case that people are unable to sustain change simply because their mental muscles are worn out.

DISCUSSION

Do you typically make decisions based more on emotion or on reason? Give an example.

....

....

How comfortable are you with the idea that emotions are an important part of decision-making?

....

....

How do you know when to let your rational brain have the final say and when to let the emotional brain do so?

....

....

Are your habit creation goals clear enough so that your RB doesn't get freaked out?

....

....

Are your habit creation goals enjoyable/rewarding enough to engage your EB?

....

....

To what extent are you relying on willpower and RB alone to carry you forward without bringing EB on board?

....

....

Identify times when EB overwhelms RB in your habit development journey. What can be done to give RB a fighting chance?

....

....

What kinds of things boost your EB? How can that insight apply to your habit development endeavors?

....

....

SHARING

OPPORTUNITY #7:

- Pray as a group for God to open the way for you to share something from these lessons to help someone else.

- Keep your radar up each day for opportunities.

How this lesson can impact our Choices and Outlook

CHOICE:

1. We can choose to reject the old way of thinking that our rational brain needs to dominate our emotional brain.

2. Habit change happens more effectively when we make choices that are in harmony with how our brains actually work.

OUTLOOK:

1. We can have more confidence in ourselves when we know how to utilize our rational and emotional brains properly.

2. We can be more optimistic about our habit development success knowing how to balance our RB and EB.

ABUNDANT LIVING THOUGHT

Willpower is an exhaustible resource unless we learn how to use both parts of our brain.

STAYING POWER

LESSON EIGHT

WARM UP

Feedback: In what ways did God open the door last week for you share some part of the lessons with someone else?

....

....

....

....

Choose one or both questions to discuss (if in group setting)
or write out your answers on a separate sheet (for individual use):

1. **What is one of the blessings you've received from this group?**[69]

....

....

....

2. **Describe one of your most beloved possessions.**

....

....

....

"Life is always a battle. But life is always worth it."

LYNDA NORDYKE HAMBLETON

DISCOVERY

I remember the time I was invited to give an outdoor sermon for a church retreat. Gathered in one section of a state park, the congregation included people of all ages, from infants to the elderly. I knew the only way to hold the attention of such a motley crowd was to tell a story from nature. The one I shared focused on the life of a humble bumble bee.

To add interest, I decided to dress the part and act it out. I donned homemade antennae, large cardboard wings, face-paint, and black leggings. To cap the effect I made appropriate buzzing sounds as I ran in circles outdoors flapping like a bee who got a D in flight school.

It was an early morning service and I hadn't taken into account the perilous combination of abundant dew and the fact that my old sneakers lacked any semblance of a tread. The third time I buzzed the crowd I got a bit too vigorous and lost it. My feet flew out from under me and I crash landed. The antennae bent crazily and shifted onto my left ear. The left wing crumpled under my body and the right one tore as I frantically tried to break my fall. I sat there stunned, waiting to be carted off to the beehive ICU.

> *One of the biggest threats to long-term success in habit creation is a loss of motivation.*

Jesus also preached outdoors and told stories from nature with much greater skill and far more dignity. To engage the large crowd, he shared the "Parable of the Sower," one of his classics:

> *"A farmer went out to plant some seeds. As he scattered them across his field, some seeds fell on a footpath, and the birds came and ate them. Other seeds fell on shallow soil with underlying rock. The seeds sprouted quickly because the soil was shallow. But the plants soon wilted under the hot sun, and since they didn't have deep roots, they died. Other seeds fell among thorns that grew up and choked out the tender plants. Still other seeds fell on fertile soil, and they produced a crop that was thirty, sixty, and even a hundred times as much as had been planted!" (Matthew 13:3-8, NLT).*

The footpath seeds are people who hear, don't really understand, and therefore fail to sprout. Shallow soil seeds are initially enthusiastic, but because they don't put down roots, they eventually wilt. The thorn seeds are choked out by the cares and pressures of the world. The fertile soil seeds both understand and carefully implement what they've heard and therefore flourish (see Matthew 13:18-23).

The purpose of this lesson is to provide information that can help you become a fertile soil seed as you seek to create abundant living habits in your life. The goal is for you to put down deep roots, have staying power, and thrive.

One of the biggest threats to long-term success in habit creation is a loss of motivation. We run low on gas and lose momentum toward our goals. When we don't get immediate results, our energy flags. Recovering and sustaining motivation is crucial to attaining your purpose. So how can that happen? What are the keys?

What we need most is a customized motivation plan. Some people think of motivation as something you either have or you don't and there's not much you can do about it. Not so. You can put together a strategy to intentionally build motivation into your life for the long haul. The following are some important tips that have helped others. Consider them carefully and select what is most relevant and helpful for you. We want to give you the best shot at completing your own race!

1. **Tap into both kinds of motivation – intrinsic and extrinsic.** Intrinsic is motivation from within. It comes from whatever gives us an inner sense of satisfaction, fulfillment, joy, and accomplishment. Extrinsic motivation comes from outside ourselves and includes rewards and affirmation from others. It is best to utilize both types in your plan with priority being given to intrinsic because it is more subject to your control and will last longer.

2. **Make sure that the positive inputs from pursuing your new habit outweigh the negatives.** Develop creative ways to glean positive energy by focusing on short-term gains and bright spots. Divide your goal into tiny steps that are easily achieved. Keep a success journal where you log all the times you made progress in your habit creation journey.[70]

3. **Make a picture collage that represents your goal** in an engaging, compelling way and put it in a prominent place.[71] Make several. You can also use visual representations of your habit goal as screensavers and wallpaper on your media devices.

4. **Study what has motivated you in the past.** Examine your own heart, look back on previous experiences, and come up with a personalized list of motivators that you can apply here.

5. **Shore up your support system.** Although American culture promotes going it alone as a virtue, change happens best in the context of a personal support system. People who arrange for others to help them in their habit creation efforts are not weak, but wise and strong.

Researchers have proven again and again that social support dramatically increases the chances of success. One study found that participants in a weight-loss program who went solo had a 76 percent completion rate but only 24 percent were able to maintain their progress. Other participants who recruited friends for support had a 95 percent completion rate and 66 percent maintained their weight loss for the six months of the survey.[72]

Author M. J. Ryan writes,
"Support comes in all kinds of forms –
someone who's been there before you who
can help you avoid pitfalls; a partner who will
practice with you; a group of people who are
all working on the same thing; a friend who
you report to; a coach who helps you stay
accountable to yourself; a therapist who can
help you uncover long-buried feelings."[73]

Try to find people to provide support who have empathy, the ability to listen well, and are non-judgmental. It is helpful if you identify for them exactly what type of support you want: "I need someone to hold my feet to the fire on deadlines" or "I just need someone to dump my frustrations on periodically who won't take it personally." This avoids a mismatch between what they offer and what you actually need.[74] Of course, avoid naysayers.

The urgent phone call came in about 7:20 p.m. on a Tuesday evening from our daughter. She was providing ongoing support for a friend who was training for the Disney World Princess Half Marathon. This night they were doing a run/walk at a local outdoor park.

The friend was crossing a wooden walkway over a pond when her driver's license accidentally fell out of her pocket and against all odds slipped sideways through a quarter inch space in the wooden slats. Last seen, it was floating beyond reach. Could I help?

I hurried into the garage, duct taped a plastic measuring cup onto a pole, and taped that onto another pole to create a "License Retrieval System" about twelve feet long. On route it stuck out of the car window like a mutant antenna with a glandular problem. Alas, by the time we arrived the license had drifted only inches too far once again. The friend thanked us profusely nonetheless.

On race day, she not only had our daughter in attendance, but friends and relatives showed up to cheer her on. She later stated that the various types of support made all the difference. The same is true for the habit development race you are now running. Support matters.

> *The Scriptures offer this sage advice,*
> *"And let us consider how we may*
> *spur one another on*
> *toward love and good deeds."*
>
> **HEBREWS 10:24, NIV**

6. **Learn how to deal with urges.**[75] Urges to return to old patterns of thinking and behaving are very real and can drain the life out of your habit creation efforts if you regularly succumb. They cannot be stopped, but you can plan now how to deal with them when they arise and even lessen their intensity and frequency. Here are some issues to consider.

   a. What *emotional states* tend to trigger your urges? Is it when you are especially tired, upset, fearful, lonely, discouraged, tense, bored? If so, you can be on special alert when such feelings and conditions arise.

   b. What environmental cues might set off the urge? By "environment" I mean the surroundings or situations you find yourself in. For many individuals their habit is simply on *autopilot* when those surroundings or situations occur. They do it without really thinking much about it.

      In one study, 100 people were offered free popcorn if they would watch previews for fifteen minutes in a movie theater. Bags of fresh popcorn and bags of stale, one week old, popcorn were given out at random. Researchers kept track of how much popcorn each person consumed.

      Individuals who rarely ordered popcorn at the movies ate a lot more fresh popcorn than they did stale. The surprising thing was that individuals who always ordered popcorn at the movies ate just as much stale as they did fresh. Their actions were not based on the taste of the popcorn, but on the automatic nature of their habit. They did it without thinking.[76]

Many habits fit into this category. They are triggered by the context rather than by an intentional desire to engage in the behavior. Willpower or commitment is not the issue because it is almost mindless.

So how do you cope? First, as much as possible, avoid places where the autopilot is triggered. Change the context. Secondly, if that is not possible, vary the pattern. Researchers discovered that simply telling participants to eat popcorn with their non-dominant hand stopped them from eating the stale popcorn, too. Decide ahead of time to throw a wrench into the pattern by making the behavior more difficult or awkward to perform.[77]

c. Develop a *competing response.* This is an activity that you engage in that makes it impossible to carry out the urge whenever it tugs at you.[78] For instance, you have a strong urge to dump on your spouse all of the hassles from work as soon as you arrive home. A competing response might be to go to the bathroom to freshen up as soon as you walk in the door so you can calm down. Or drink a couple of glasses of water to keep you swallowing rather than talking. This is also known as "active diversion."[79] Distract yourself. You can also do the exact opposite of what you want to avoid; for instance, choosing to listen rather than speak.

d. Beware of what are called *"facilitating thoughts"* such as, "Just this once," "I deserve to indulge," "I need to engage in this old habit in order to cope today." Answer the following questions:

"How will I feel later if I give in to my urges?"

"What consequences might I suffer if I give in?"

"Will the negatives outweigh the positives in the long run if I give in?"[80]

e. *Wait them out.* Urges come in waves, reaching an apex and then receding. They usually last a minute or two. You will not die if you refuse to indulge. Take it one urge at a time.

7. **Read information related to your goal** to make it more real and interesting.[81]

8. **Get moving.** Remind yourself why you are pursuing this new habit and then act on it even when you don't feel like it. Many times motivation comes *after* we get moving. Harvard Physiologist Jerome Bruner observes, "You're more likely to act yourself into feeling, than feel yourself into action."[82]

9. **Allow yourself a time-out periodically** to wallow in frustration, perhaps fifteen minutes, then move on. Recognize that there is a natural ebb and flow to life. We can't be "up" all the time.

> *Love is the most powerful of all motivators. Regarding your own abundant life journey, stay with it because you love God, yourself, your family, your friends, and life itself.*

10. Do it for love. Edward Deci relates the following story.

"[A] woman… began smoking in her early teens because all of her friends were doing it and she thought it helped her look grown-up and sexy. She became quite dependent on her cigarettes, and by the time she was twenty-one, she smoked three packs a day. She had tried to stop a couple of times, with no more success at quitting tobacco than the advertising executive who occasionally 'gave up' drinking.

But then something happened for this young woman that changed all that. She fell in love with an attractive, outgoing man with plans and dreams. He was a nonsmoker, and although he did not prod her about her own smoking, he represented an example for her. And even more, as she began thinking about their life together, with babies growing into adults, she began to think of how her smoking could hurt them as well as herself.

She, in fact, stopped smoking, and although it was not easy, it did last. Why? Because she had found a truly meaningful personal reason, and when she did, she had a deep determination to carry through." [83]

Love is the most powerful of all motivators. Regarding your own abundant life journey, stay with it because you love God, yourself, your family, your friends, and life itself.

> *"God can do anything, you know –
> far more than you could ever imagine or guess
> or request in your wildest dreams! He does it not
> by pushing us around but by working within us,
> his Spirit deeply and gently within us."*
>
> **EPHESIANS 3:20, THE MESSAGE**

Hopefully you were able to find some keys in this lesson regarding how to become one of the "fertile soil seeds" that Jesus spoke about in his parable and thrive in your choice of an abundant living lifestyle.

NOTES:

You're more likely to act yourself into feeling, than feel yourself into action."

JEROME BRUNER

DISCUSSION

What is one of your favorite outdoor stories or experiences?

....

....

What motivates you to accomplish tasks? How can that apply to your habit creation journey?

....

....

Do you depend more on intrinsic or extrinsic motivation? How can you bring those more into balance?

....

....

Do you find the process of developing a new habit at times draining? What helps keep you going?

....

....

If you kept a new habit success journal, what might be one of the entries?

....

....

Discuss what your support system could potentially include.

....

....

Imagine a strong urge to engage in your old habit or abandon a new one. What plan can you come with now to overcome that urge when it occurs?

....

....

What role can love play in motivating you to accomplish your habit creation goal?

....

....

SHARING

OPPORTUNITY #8:

- Pray as a group for God to open the way for you to share something from these lessons to help someone else.

- Keep your radar up each day for opportunities.

How this lesson can impact our Choices and Outlook

CHOICE:

1. We can choose to create a motivation plan that taps into both intrinsic and extrinsic sources.

2. Deciding to put a support system in place will significantly increase our chances of success.

3. Learning about how to deal with urges now will enable us to make the right choices when they occur.

OUTLOOK:

1. Picturing ourselves as *fertile soil seeds* can provide a tremendous boost to our sense of optimism regarding the future.

2. Love is a motivation for new habit formation that can outlast all others.

ABUNDANT LIVING THOUGHT
You can put together a strategy to build motivation into your life for the long haul.

DON'T STOP BUILDING NOW
FILL IN THE MISSING PIECES

You already have a number of key building blocks in place from what you learned in this Part 2 of "Creating Healthy Habits for Life." To get the rest of the pieces be sure to pick up part 1. It is Guide #1 in the CREATION Health Life Guide Series.

CREATING HEALTHY HABITS FOR LIFE
Part 1
C·R·E·A·T·I·O·N
C·R·E·A·T·I·O·N Health
LIFE GUIDE #1
For Individual Study and Small Group Use

CREATING HEALTHY HABITS FOR LIFE
Part 2
C·R·E·A·T·I·O·N
C·R·E·A·T·I·O·N Health
LIFE GUIDE #7
For Individual Study and Small Group Use

PARTS 1&2: **CHOICE & OUTLOOK**

ABOUT THE AUTHOR

Kim Johnson is a popular writer, speaker, and fervent advocate for holistic living. As the author of three books, eleven lesson series, and many articles, his writings focus on healthy living and spiritual connectedness. His materials have been used in hundreds of churches throughout North America and internationally as well.

Johnson is an ordained minister with more than 35 years of experience as a parish pastor and church administrator. Over the years, his work with parishioners emphasized principles of whole-person health as a path to optimum mental, physical, social, and spiritual well-being. His later work with pastors and church leaders emphasized skill development such as vision casting, goal setting, support systems, relationship management, and accountability. Johnson has put his experience of working with pastors and parishioners to use in the CREATION Health Life Guide Series by creating a resource ideally suited for use in churches, small groups or individual study.

Johnson holds a Master of Divinity degree and received his Bachelor of Arts in theology. He currently serves as Director of Resource Development for churches in the state of Florida. His personal interests include reading, classical music, art and book festivals, kayaking, traveling, volunteering, and small group study. He and his wife Ann make their home in Orlando.

Author Acknowledgements: It has been a great privilege for me to be associated with the team of dedicated individuals who helped in various ways to make these CREATION Health Life Guides available. I would like to single out my wife Ann and daughter Stefanie, whose feedback and suggestions were always characterized by unfailing support and clear-eyed honesty. I have also received invaluable guidance and encouragement from Mike Cauley, Tim Nichols, Nick Howard, and Jim Epperson. Finally, I want to thank the group of local pastors who met with me personally and provided a wonderful forum for evaluating the lesson drafts.

NOTES

1. Garry Poole, *The Complete Book of Questions* (Grand Rapids, MI: Zondervan, 2003), 20.

2. Garry Poole, *The Complete Book of Questions*, 89.

3. Garry Poole, *The Complete Book of Questions*, 82.

4. Jeremy Gutshce, *Exploiting Chaos* ((New York, NY: Gotham Books, 2009), 96.

5. Jeremy Gutshce, *Exploiting Chaos*, 99.

6. Jeremy Gutshce, *Exploiting Chaos*, 222.

7. M. J. Ryan, *This Year I Will* (New York, NY: Broadway Books, 2006), 174.

8. John C. Maxwell, *Attitude 101* (Nashville, TN: Thomas Nelson, 2003), 76-81; M. J. Ryan, *This Year I Will*, 207.

9. John C. Maxwell, *Attitude 101*, 56-57.

10. Barbara Ann Kipfer, *4,000 Questions for Getting to Know Anyone and Everyone* (New York: NY: Random House, 2004), 50.

11. Daniel Coyle, *The Talent Code* (New York, NY: Bantam Dell, 2009), 32.

12. Craig Freudenrich, PhD and Robynne Boyd, *"How Your Brain Works,"* http://science.howstuffworks.com/environmental/life/human-biology/brain1.htm.

13. *"Neurons and Synapses,"* http://www.human-memory.net/brain_neurons.html.

14. Daniel Coyle, *The Talent Code*, 32, 36, 40-41.

15. Daniel Coyle, *The Talent Code*, 40.

16. Daniel Coyle, *The Talent Code*, 32-33, 40-41.

17. Nervous System Notes, http://www.methuen.k12.ma.us/daberns/Anatomy/Chapter%207/nervous%20system%20notes.htm; Daniel Coyle, *The Talent Code*, 68; Glenn Karisch, "Talent – Under The Microscope," (Live Fitness: August 11, 2010), http://www.leecountylive.com/fitness%2019.htm.

18. Daniel Coyle, *The Talent Code*, 43-45.

19. "Learning and thinking: what science tells us about teaching" (August 2001), http://www.studentsfriend.com/onhist/learning.html; Daniel Coyle, *The Talent Code*,78-80.

20. Daniel Coyle, *The Talent Code*, 18, 43-44.

21. Daniel Coyle, *The Talent Code*, 40.

22. M. J. Ryan, *This Year I Will*, 205.

23. Barbara Ann Kipfer, *4000 Questions for Getting to Know Anyone and Everyone*, 10.

24. Garry Poole, *The Complete Book of Questions*, 118.

25. Mark F. Weinstein, *Habitually Great* (Charleston, SC: BookSurge, 2009), 39-40.

26. Mark F. Weinstein, *Habitually Great*, 40, 44-45.

27. Hyrum W. Smith, *What Matters Most* (New York, NY: Simon & Schuster, 2000), 154-155.

28. M. J. Ryan, *This Year I Will*, 60-61.

29. M. J. Ryan, *This Year I Will*, 62.

30. Jonah Lehrer, *How We Decide* (New York, NY: Houghton, Mifflin, Harcourt, 2009), 52.

31. Chip Heath and Dan Heath, Switch (New York, NY: Broadway Books, 2010), 164.

32. M. J. Ryan, *This Year I Will*, 64-65.

33. Carol S. Dweck, PhD, *Mindset* (New York, NY: Ballantine Books, 2006), 16.

34. Stephen R. Covey, *7 Habits of Highly Effective People* (New York, NY: Simon and Schuster, 1989), 70.

35. Carol S. Dweck, PhD, *Mindset*, 40.

36. Daniel Coyle, Talent Code, 51.

37. Carol S. Dweck, PhD, *Mindset*, 52.

38. Geoffrey Colvin, "What it takes to be great," October 19, 2006, http://money.cnn.com/magazines/fortune/fortune_archive/2006/10/30/8391794/index.htm .

39. Steve Sheely, *Ice-Breakers and Heart-Warmers* (Littleton, CO: Serendipity House, 1996), 50.

40. Barbara Ann Kipfer, *4,000 Questions for Getting to Know Anyone and Everyone*, 117.

41. James Claiborn, PhD and Cherry Pedrick, RN, *The Habit Change Workbook* (Oakland, CA: New Harbinger Publications, Inc., 2001), 88-91; Reneau Z. Peurifoy, *Anxiety, Phobias, and Panic* (Life Skills, 1992), 77-86; Mark F. Weinstein, *Habitually Great*, 119-120.

42. Hal Stone and Sidra Stone, *Embracing Your Inner Critic* (New York, NY: HarperCollins, 1993) 19; Kristin Neff, PhD, *Self-Compassion* (New York, NY: HarperCollins, 2011), 112.

43. Hal Stone and Sidra Stone, *Embracing Your Inner Critic*, 7-12.

44. American Autoimmune Related Diseases Association, http://www.aarda.org/q_and_a.php.

45. M. J. Ryan, *This Year I Will*, 170-171.

46. Kristin Neff, PhD, *Self-Compassion*, 116.

47. Kristin Neff, PhD, *Self-Compassion*, 119.

48. Kristin Neff, PhD, *Self-Compassion*, 42.

49. Barbara Ann Kipfer, *4,000 Questions for Getting to Know Anyone and Everyone*, 36.

50. Gary Poole, *The Complete Book of Questions*, 73.

51. Mark F. Weinstein, *Habitually Great*, 190.

52. Stephen R. Covey, *The 7 Habits of Highly Effective People*, 151.

53. Brian Bartes, "Big Rocks," http://superperformance.com/bigrocks.php.

54. M. J. Ryan, *This Year I Will*, 115.

55. Celetine Chua, *"7 Simple Ways To Say 'No'"* (The Personal Excellence Blog: August 3, 2010), http://zenhabits.net/say-no/.

56. Barbara Ann Kipfer, *4000 Questions for Getting to Know Anyone and Everyone*, 89.

57. Garry Poole, *The Complete Book of Questions*, 49.

58. Jonah Lehrer, *How We Decide*, 13-16.

59. Jonah Lehrer, *How We Decide*, xv-xvi, 9-11.

60. Chip Heath and Dan Heath, *Switch* (New York, NY: Broadway Books, 2010), 7-8.

61. Jonah Lehrer, *How We Decide*, 23.

62. Jonah Lehrer, *How We Decide*, 18, 203.

63. Chip Heath and Dan Heath, *Switch*, 17, 53-54.

64. Chip Heath and Dan Heath, *Switch*, 50.

65. Chip Heath and Dan Heath, *Switch*, 10-11.

66. M. J. Ryan, *This Year I Will*, 27-28.

67. Chip Heath and Dan Heath, *Switch*, 130-131.

68. Chip Heath and Dan Heath, *Switch*, 8.

69. Steve Sheely, *Ice-Breakers and Heart-Warmers* (Littleton, CO: Serendipity House, 1996), 87.

70. "Self Motivation Techniques: Tactics to keep your career change motivation high," http://www.how-to-change-careers.com/self-motivation-techniques.html.

71. Steve Mueller, "Proven Motivation Tactics to Boost your Motivation,"http://www.planetofsuccess.com/motivationtechniques/.

72. Robert A. Emmons, PhD, *Thanks: How Practicing Gratitude Can Make You Happier* (New York, NY: Houghton Mifflin Company, 2008), 200.

73. M. J. Ryan, *This Year I Will*, 104.

74. James O. Prochaska, PhD, John C. Norcross, PhD, Carlo C. DeClemente, PhD, *Changing for Good* (New York, NY: HarperCollins, 1994), 142.

75. James O. Prochaska, PhD, John C. Norcross, PhD, Carlo C. DeClemente, PhD, *Changing for Good*, 176-190.

76. Heidi Grant Halvorson PhD, "Why Willpower Isn't Enough" (October 5, 2011), http://www.huffingtonpost.com/heidi-grant-halvorson-phd/willpower-bad-habits_b_993968.html.

77. Heidi Grant Halvorson PhD, "Why Willpower Isn't Enough" (October 5, 2011), http://www.huffingtonpost.com/heidi-grant-halvorson-phd/willpower-bad-habits_b_993968.html.

78. James Claiborn, PhD and Cherry Pedrick, RN, *The Habit Change*, 33, 60.

79. James O. Prochaska, PhD, John C. Norcross, PhD, Carlo C. DeClemente, PhD, *Changing for Good*, 177.

80. Robert Westermeyer, PhD, "Coping With Urges," http://www.moderation.org/faq/coping.shtml.

81. "Just can't get motivated?" http://www.self-improvement-mentor.com/self-motivation-techniques.html.

82. Michael Dolpies, *Motion Before Motivation* (Lexington, KY: Ocean View Publishing, LLC, 2010), xii.

83. Edward L. Deci, *Why We Do What We Do* (New York, NY: Penguin Books, 1995), 165.

RESOURCES

LEAD YOUR COMMUNITY
TO HEALTHY
LIVING

With C·R·E·A·T·I·O·N Health
Seminars, Books, & Resources

SHOP OUR ONLINE STORE AT:

CREATIONHealth.com

FOR MANY MORE RESOURCES

"CREATION Health has made a tremendous impact as part of the health ministries of our church and has also changed my life! We plan to continue an ongoing CREATION Health seminar at Forest Lake Church."

~ Derek Morris, Senior Pastor,
Forest Lake Church

SEMINAR MATERIALS

INCLUDES
ONLINE TRAINING

Leader Guide

Everything a leader needs to conduct this seminar successfully, including key questions to facilitate group discussion and PowerPoint™ presentations for each of the eight principles.

Participant Guide

A study guide with essential information from each of the eight lessons along with outlines, self assessments, and questions for people to fill-in as they follow along.

Small Group Kit

It's easy to lead a small group using the CREATION Health videos, the Small Group Leaders Guide and the Small Group Discussion Guide.

Senior Guide

Share the CREATION Health principles with seniors and help them be healthier and happier as they live life to the fullest.

Self-Assessment

This instrument raises awareness about how CREATION Healthy a person is in each of the eight major areas of wellness.

Pregnancy Guides

Expert advice on how to be CREATION Healthy while expecting.

GET ORGANIZED!

Tote Bag

A convenient way for bringing CREATION Health materials to and from class.

Smartphone App

The free CREATION Health App supplies daily health tips, weekly CREATION Conversation videos, and refreshing virtual vacations to break away from your day.

Presentation Folder

Keep CREATION Health notes and resources organized and in one place.

Pocket Guide

A tool for keeping people committed to living all of the CREATION Health principles daily.

MARKETING MATERIALS

Postcards, Posters, Stationary, and more

You can effectively advertise and generate community excitement about your CREATION Health seminar with a wide range of available marketing materials such as enticing postcards, flyers, posters, and more.

CREATION Health Discovery (Softcover)

CREATION Health Discovery takes the 8 essential principles of CREATION Health and melds them together to form the blueprint for the health we yearn for and the life we are intended to live.

CREATION Health Breakthrough (Hardcover)

Blending science and lifestyle recommendations, Monica Reed, MD, prescribes eight essentials that will help reverse harmful health habits and prevent disease. Discover how intentional choices, rest, environment, activity, trust, relationships, outlook, and nutrition can put a person on the road to wellness. Features a three-day total body rejuvenation therapy and four-phase life transformation plan.

CREATION Health Devotional (English: Hardcover / Spanish: Softcover)

Stories change lives. Stories can inspire health and healing. In this devotional you will discover stories about experiencing God's grace in the tough times, God's delight in triumphant times, and God's presence in peaceful times. Based on the eight timeless principles of wellness: Choice, Rest, Environment, Activity, Trust, Interpersonal relationships, Outlook, Nutrition.

CREATION Health Devotional for Women (English)

Written for women by women, the *CREATION Health Devotional for Women* is based on the principles of whole-person wellness represented in CREATION Health. Spirits will be lifted and lives rejuvenated by the message of each unique chapter. This book is ideal for women's prayer groups, to give as a gift, or just to buy for your own edification and encouragement.

8 Secrets of a Healthy 100 (Softcover)

Can you imagine living to a Healthy 100 years of age? Dr. Des Cummings Jr., explores the principles practiced by the All-stars of Longevity to live longer and more abundantly. Take a journey through the 8 Secrets and you will be inspired to imagine living to a Healthy 100.

Forgive To Live (English: Hardcover / Spanish: Softcover)

In Forgive to Live Dr. Tibbits presents the scientifically proven steps for forgiveness – taken from the first clinical study of its kind conducted by Stanford University and Florida Hospital.

Forgive To Live Workbook (Softcover)

This interactive guide will show you how to forgive – insight by insight, step by step – in a workable plan that can effectively reduce your anger, improve your health, and put you in charge of your life again, no matter how deep your hurts.

Forgive To Live Devotional (Hardcover)

In his powerful new devotional Dr. Dick Tibbits reveals the secret to forgiveness. This compassionate devotional is a stirring look at the true meaning of forgiveness. Each of the 56 spiritual insights includes motivational Scripture, an inspirational prayer, and two thought-provoking questions. The insights are designed to encourage your journey as you begin to *Forgive to Live*.

Forgive To Live God's Way (Softcover)

Forgiveness is so important that our very lives depend on it. Churches teach us that we should forgive, but how do you actually learn to forgive? In this spiritual workbook noted author, psychologist, and ordained minister Dr. Dick Tibbits takes you step-by-step through an eight-week forgiveness format that is easy to understand and follow.

Forgive To Live Leader's Guide

Perfect for your community, church, small group or other settings.

The Forgive to Live Leader's Guide Includes:

- 8 Weeks of pre-designed PowerPoint™ presentations.
- Professionally designed customizable marketing materials and group handouts on CD-Rom.
- Training directly from author of Forgive to Live Dr. Dick Tibbits across 6 audio CDs.
- Media coverage DVD.
- CD-Rom containing all files in digital format for easy home or professional printing.
- A copy of the first study of its kind conducted by Stanford University and Florida Hospital showing a link between decreased blood pressure and forgiveness.

52 Ways to Feel Great Today (Softcover)

Wouldn't you love to feel great today? Changing your outlook and injecting energy into your day often begins with small steps. In *52 Ways to Feel Great Today*, you'll discover an abundance of simple, inexpensive, fun things you can do to make a big difference in how you feel today and every day. Tight on time? No problem. Each chapter is written as a short, easy-to-implement idea. Every idea is supported by at least one true story showing how helpful implementing the idea has proven to someone a lot like you. The stories are also included to encourage you to be as inventive, imaginative, playful, creative, or adventuresome as you can.

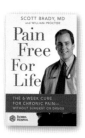

Pain Free For Life (Hardcover)

In *Pain Free For Life*, Scott C. Brady, MD, – founder of Florida Hospital's Brady Institute for Health – shares for the first time with the general public his dramatically successful solution for chronic back pain, Fibromyalgia, chronic headaches, Irritable bowel syndrome and other "impossible to cure" pains. Dr. Brady leads pain-racked readers to a pain-free life using powerful mind-body-spirit strategies used at the Brady Institute – where more than 80 percent of his chronic-pain patients have achieved 80-100 percent pain relief within weeks.

If Today Is All I Have (Softcover)

At its heart, Linda's captivating account chronicles the struggle to reconcile her three dreams of experiencing life as a "normal woman" with the tough realities of her medical condition. Her journey is punctuated with insights that are at times humorous, painful, provocative, and life-affirming.

SuperSized Kids (Hardcover)

In *SuperSized Kids*, Walt Larimore, MD, and Sherri Flynt, MPH, RD, LD, show how the mushrooming childhood obesity epidemic is destroying children's lives, draining family resources, and pushing America dangerously close to a total healthcare collapse – while also explaining, step by step, how parents can work to avert the coming crisis by taking control of the weight challenges facing every member of their family.

SuperFit Family Challenge – Leader's Guide

Perfect for your community, church, small group or other settings.

The SuperFit Family Challenge Leader's Guide Includes:
- 8 Weeks of pre-designed PowerPoint™ presentations.
- Professionally designed marketing materials and group handouts from direct mailers to reading guides.
- Training directly from Author Sherri Flynt, MPH, RD, LD, across 6 audio CDs.
- Media coverage and FAQ on DVD.

LIVE YOUR LIFE
TO THE FULLEST

C·R·E·A·T·I·O·N Health

LIFE GUIDE SERIES

8 Guides. 8 Principles. One Powerful Message.
Packed with fresh insights on abundant living.
For Individual Study and Small Group Use.

Perfect for churches, schools, universities, and faith-based businesses.

IMAGINE...
A body that is healthy and strong,
A spirit that is vibrant and refreshed,
A life that glorifies God,
Imagine living to a **Healthy 100.**